Christmas 1995.

Lots of love

Peter Christine Alexandra
Adam and Zoe

D1612409

THE SCOTS GARD'NER

THE
SCOTS
GARD'NER

Publiſhed for the Climate of SCOTLAND
By JOHN REID Gard'ner

Introduction by
ANNETTE HOPE

The First Scottish Gardening Book
Published 1683

This edition published in Great Britain in 1988 by
MAINSTREAM PUBLISHING COMPANY (EDINBURGH) LTD
7 Albany Street
Edinburgh EH1 3UG

British Library Cataloguing in Publication Data
Reid, John, *fl. 1620*
The Scot's gard'ner.
I. Title
635

ISBN 1-85158-125-1

The publisher gratefully acknowledges the financial assistance of the
Scottish Arts Council in the publication of this volume.

Typeset in Garamond
Printed in Great Britain by Butler & Tanner, Frome, Somerset

INTRODUCTION

The Scots Gard'ner is the first gardening book to be written by a Scot, with specifically Scottish conditions in mind. Its Appendix, "Shewing how to use the Fruits of the Garden", also has some claim to be called the first Scottish cookery book. This volume has therefore a certain historical importance.

But if that were not the case, it would still stand apart from contemporary early gardening literature. John Reid engages his readers with such intelligent candour, directness of style, and business-like advice barely suppressing enthusiasm, that on every page there is evidence of a vigorous personality at work.

Who was he? Far from being a shadowy, obscure figure about whom very little could be known (as was once believed), his life is surprisingly well documented. For a start, we have his own account written in his last year, and now in the possession of his own descendants in Philadelphia. State records both in Scotland and New Jersey add to our knowledge. And within his book itself we can find clues which help to round out a portrait.

He was born on 13th February 1655/56 – the double date indicates a difference between the Scottish and English calendars of the time, the Scots having adopted the Gregorian calendar on January 1st, 1600, as opposed to the English changeover which occurred only in 1751 – at Niddry Castle, near Winchburgh, not far from Edinburgh, where both his grandfather and father were gardeners.

The boy probably received some schooling at the local parish school at Kirkliston, but when he was almost nine his father died, and it became necessary to choose a career. Rejecting the family profession, he engaged himself as apprentice to an Edinburgh vintner, whose service he entered when he was nearly eleven. However, the apprenticeship was never completed, for upon the death of his employer in November 1773 he returned to Niddry.

His mother had by this time remarried, and now at last Reid was "persuaded to learn the old but pleasant art of Gard'nery". He seems to have agreed to try the work for a year, for he later wrote that at the end of that period, "after I had seen what I could expect . . . (I) went to the celebrated gardens of Hamilton where I dived into that noble science. . . ." He also found himself drawn to Quakerism and became a convert.

After a year at Hamilton he moved to Drummond Castle, in Perthshire. Here he found extensive gardens in the Italian, French, and Dutch styles, but again he only remained a twelvemonth. Then came his most important move to date: on 27th November 1676 he began work at Lawers, or Fordie – also in Perthshire. He spent four years at Lawers, perhaps as head gardener. At all events he now had leisure enough to begin writing his book, and money enough to marry. His wife, Margaret Miller, also a Quaker, was ten years his senior. Reid was now twenty-two. On 24th January 1679/80 their first daughter, Anna, was born.

In 1680 came another move, to Shank, a pleasant and fertile estate on a bank of the South Esk Water in East Lothian, belonging to Sir George Mackenzie of Rosehaugh, Lord Advocate of Scotland – famous in Covenanting history as "the Bloody Mackenzie". There is no evidence that Reid ever worked on Mackenzie's other estate at Avoch in Ross-shire.

We find the family still at Shank at the beginning of 1683. There were now two daughters, Anna and Helena, and a third child was expected in May. *The Scots Gard'ner* was ready for publication later in the year. Reid had a good, secure job and a pleasant house. It seems curious that he should choose this moment to emigrate, and he is silent about his reasons, but the immediate impetus was probably supplied by a pamphlet published in Edinburgh in the early part of the year, entitled *A Brief Account of the Province of New Jersey, in America: Published by the Scots Proprietors Having Interest there. For the Information of such as may have a Desire to Transport themselves, or their Families thither. Wherein the Nature and Advantage of, and Interest in a Foreign Plantation to this Country is Demonstrated.*

Reading it, Reid's apparently sudden decision seems less surprising. The author made a persuasive case for emigration, with promises of an easier life than at home. The climate in the new colony was good, the soil rich and fruitful. There were woodlands, meadows, and well-matured pastures. Game of all sorts, including turkey and bear, were to be had for the shooting, so that a family need never want meat. The coastline was sheltered, the sea teeming with fish. The Indians were friendly. Religious toleration for all Christians was promised, since the majority of Proprietors were Quakers. People going out as ordinary servants to the Proprietors would, after four years' service from the time of their arrival, "have set out to each 25 Acres to them and theirs forever, paying 2 pence an Acre, as much Corne as will sow an Acre and a Sute of new Cloaths". A ship was scheduled to sail in late summer.

On 10th August 1683, before even *The Scots Gard'ner* was off the presses, the Reid family embarked on the Exchange and sailed for America, reaching Woodbridge, New Jersey, on 10th January 1684.

It was a bad time to arrive, during the coldest month of the year. The voyage had been long, and several passengers, including Reid's child Margaret (just eight months old), died. Hers was one of the first graves at the new settlement of Perth Amboy.

Reid's indenture actually took effect from 1st December 1684. He was engaged as an overseer to the settlement, under terms somewhat more favourable than those in the advertisement. Before sailing he had already received ten pounds from the Proprietors. Now he was granted a salary of twenty-five pounds a year, a house, eight cows, six oxen, two horses, and four sows.

In Scotland he had become proficient at laying out new estates, and now this talent was put to good use. Seconded to the post of Deputy Surveyor-General, he laid out the settlement and mapped Perth Amboy and the province of New Jersey. This gave him the chance to form an opinion of his new home, and in a letter to a friend in Edinburgh eight months after his arrival, he described his impressions. It was a brave place, he wrote, for

> Here is no outward want, especially of provisions, and if people
> were industrious they might have cloaths also within themselves
> . . . . The soyl of the country is generally a red marle earth with a
> surface of black mould (nor doth it appear what really it is to their
> eyes who cannot penetrate beyond the surface), full freighted with
> grass, pleasant herbs and flowers, and in many places little or no
> wood, but most places full of large timber, as walnut, especially
> oak; there be some places here and there in the woods, they call
> swamps, which is low Ground amidst or betwixt rising ground
> full of bushes, which holds water in winter, the most of them be
> dry in summer, but these being cleared are the richest land.

The gardener in him was fascinated by all he saw – the indigenous
plants, the crops best suited to the soil and climate, local methods
of cultivation – above all, the extraordinary fertility compared
with Scotland. "I know nothing wanting here except that good
Tradesmen, and good Husbandmen, and Labourers are scarce".
And he ends with a message for a friend: "There are a great store
of Garden herbs here. I have not had time to inquire into them all,
neither to send some of the many pleasant, (tho' to me unknown)
plants of this country, to James Sutherland, physick Gardener at
Edinburgh, but tell him, I will not forget him, when opportunity
offers".
     As soon as his indenture expired, Reid began to amass his own
estate. We find him in 1687 buying from the Proprietors ten acres
of "boggy meadow" – clearly some of the swampland whose
potential he had noted soon after his arrival. At the end of that
year he is granted a patent for two hundred acres, and names the
estate "Hortensia", moving there on 26th November 1687 with
his wife and children – Anna, Helena, and fifteen-month-old
John. In time he is also given five hundred acres of land in
consideration of service to the community as a member of the
General Assembly. In 1695, aged thirty-nine, he becomes

Surveyor-General of the province. By 1700 his total land holdings amount to over 3710 acres.

Our portrait now is almost done, and we may pause a moment and take stock. The sitter's image is emerging, incomplete certainly, but with well-defined traits which, even at a distance of 300 years, we can identify. Visibly he is an ambitious, determined man, self-educated to a level far above that of the parish school. Evidence of independent mind comes both in his choice, early in life, of a religious sect then in its infancy, and in his decision to leave Scotland for a new life in a still uncharted country. Yet he also has a strong sense of friendship and social obligation, and is probably well-liked by many – witness his election to the General Assembly and the gift of land by the community. His intelligence and powers of observation have led him into a career rather different from that of his forebears, but he retains a genuine love of plants and gardens, as we see by the naming of his estate.

Perhaps the most significant subsequent event of his life is spiritual rather than material. He had always been religious – he writes of having been "happily drawn into Quakerism by the great professions of sanctity and immediate Inspirations" in 1674, when the sect was but thirty years old. In America, Quaker propaganda had been influential in bringing new settlers. West New Jersey was at the time wholly Quaker, but in the Eastern province Reid had friends outside the Community. Nevertheless it is startling to read that, in 1703, he abandoned the "error" of nearly thirty years and followed his friend and first employer in America, George Keith, into the Church of England. The baptism may indeed have been a family affair; at all events Reid's daughter Helena married a Church of England parson two years later. His name was John Bartow, and it is through the Bartow genealogy that we have access to Reid's autobiographical sketch. The elder daughter, Anna, was already married. John Junior married in 1721 and had one child, a girl, during Reid's lifetime.

The last entry in the Bartow manuscript reads: "My daughter Anna Anderson died July 6th 1723, aged 43 years, 5 months and 12 days". Four months later, on November 16th 1723, our

Scots Gardener himself died, and was buried in the old
Topanemus cemetery, a mile west of Marlborough, not far from
his beloved Hortensia. His wife Margaret survived him five
years.

Brief as it is, this survey of Reid's life should be enough to show
that his book is far from being, as once was thought, an isolated
phenomenon springing from the brain of an uneducated
labourer. In fact it can be set firmly within a cultural context.

There had been since the 15th century a general European
revival of interest in the domestic arts, which had been slow to
reach Britain and slower to take root in Scotland, due to that
country's severe political and economic difficulties in the 16th
and 17th centuries. But though they may have been tardy in
implementing the new ideas, Scots were well aware of them. As
the need for fortified homes diminished, many noblemen had
planted pleasure gardens, following Royal example at Stirling,
Falkland, Holyrood and Linlithgow. At Reid's own birthplace,
Niddry Castle, the Setons created a great walled garden
extending over almost three acres at the beginning of the 17th
century. It was here that Reid's father and grandfather worked,
and there is an interesting link between them and the famous
garden (now restored) of Pitmedden in Aberdeenshire, which
was laid out somewhat later, in 1675. Sir Alexander Seton of
Pitmedden was already a young man of twenty when John Reid
was born, but, made fatherless in early childhood, he and his
brother had been cared for by their kinsman George Lord Seton,
Earl of Winton, who of course owned Niddry. The boys probably
spent most of their time at Winton and Seton Palace, but most
certainly must have visited Niddry, and it is pleasant to conjecture
that it was one of the Reids who first inspired in Alexander Seton
that love of gardens which led to the creation of Pitmedden.

Nevertheless, though the number of Scottish gardens might
increase, until 1683 their owners had to rely for guidance on
books written in England or France. Among the books one might
have found in a 17th century Scots nobleman's library were an
early French treatise, *Maison Rustique*, and Thomas Tusser's
Five hundred Pointes of Good Husbandrie, written in easily

memorised doggerel verse. Sir Hugh Platt's *Flores Paradisae* was
another popular book, as was John Rea's *Flora sue de Florum
Cultura* (1665), which according to Blanche Henrey (*British
Botanical and Horticultural Literature before 1800*) was the most
important treatise on gardening to be published during the
second half of the 17th century. This book resembles Reid's in
concentrating on smaller gardens, with several suggested plans.
Leonard Meager's *The English Gardener* (1670) was also aimed at
the small nobleman or private gentleman.

Without doubt the most influential gardening writer of the age
was the great John Evelyn. His first work was a translation of *Le
Jardinier Francois* by Nicolas de Bonnefons (1651). Under the
title *The French Gardener* it appeared in December 1658, and
there are passages in *The Scots Gard'ner* which suggest that Reid ·
borrowed more than his title from this work. Evelyn's second
book, *Silva*, discussed in much detail the cultivation of trees, and
had an appendix containing a *Kalendarium Hortense* – the first
gardener's calendar to be published in English. The second was of
course Reid's own.

Evelyn is one of three authors to whom Reid refers by name in
his book. The others are Thomas Langford, whose *Plain and full
instructions to raise all sorts of fruit-trees that prosper in England*
seems to have been widely read, and Moses Cook. His book, *The
manner of raising, ordering, and improving forrest-trees* (1676)
was a highly scientific treatise, including many tables and
mathematical calculations – something new in gardening
literature. "I have used arithmetick the more", he wrote,
"because it is so usefull to the ingenious planter". It was a point of
view which Reid shared.

It should be recognised that although Reid's book had no
forerunners in Scotland, the study of plants was far from
unknown here. It is curious how the year 1683 seems to run
through the story. Not only was it the year of *The Scots Gard'ner*
and Reid's departure for New Jersey, it also saw the death of a
celebrated Scots botanist and the publication of a book by Reid's
friend, James Sutherland (the man to whom Reid had promised to
send seeds from New Jersey).

The botanist was Robert Morison, a native Aberdonian who at the end of his life was Professor of Botany at Oxford. Before his untimely death (he was knocked down by the pole of a coach in the Strand) he had published an extremely influential catalogue of the plants in the Royal Garden at Blois, where he had been at one time a director.

James Sutherland's book may well have been inspired by Morison's *Hortus Regius Blesensis (Praeludiorum Botanicorum Pars Prior)*. From 1670 to 1690 he was Intendant of the small physic garden set up by two leading Edinburgh doctors, Andrew Balfour and Robert Sibbald. He was also a keen botanist. His *Hortus Medicus Edinburgensis* (1683) is subtitled *A Catalogue of the Plants in the Physical Garden at Edinburgh Containing Their most proper Latin and English Names; With an English Alphabetical Index*. The fact that his book was on sale at the physic garden suggests that the latter (later to become the Royal Botanic Gardens of Edinburgh) was even at that early date open to visitors.

Sutherland's connection with Reid is shadowy. They were at least acquaintances; not only did Reid refer to Sutherland in the letter already quoted, he also directs readers of *The Scots Gard'ner* to him: "If you would be further satisfied in the varieties of plants, consult the Learned and most Ingenious Mr James Sutherland's Catalogue Phisick Gardener at Edinburgh".

If the two were more than acquaintances, we may have the answer to the question of how Reid acquired his wide reading and knowledge of surveying. It seems unlikely that any employer would give his gardener free run of the library, especially considering Reid's frequent changes of job. Through Sutherland, however, he would have had access to books used at the physic garden. The reference to Cook's work, published in 1676, shows how up-to-date was his reading. It is certainly interesting to note that Robert Sibbald, one of the founders of the Physic Garden looked after by Sutherland, gave to the College of Physicians a copy of Evelyn's *Kalendarium Hortense*.

This leads to a consideration of Reid's originality. He must have got the idea for his *Gardener's Calendar* from Evelyn. He may have drawn on Cook for his mathematical approach to garden layout. Was he then a snapper-up of other people's thoughts, cobbling together things he had read elsewhere with adaptions to suit Scotland? The answer, I think, is No. Although drawing on (and acknowledging) other sources, he is obviously writing from his own experience, and it is here that his originality lies. He is a born teacher, anxious to enter into dialogue with his readers, for he knows that the best way of learning is by example. So he constantly reminds us of his presence. "I have tried to . . . I know the contrary from experience . . . I am not for . . . For my part . . ." – it is just as if we were actually walking through a garden with him, turning aside to see how the grafts on the cherry-tree are doing, planning a new walk, pulling up a stray weed "to keep all neat". Occasionally he shares his personal preferences with us. "The Kitchen Garden is the best of all Gardens . . ." then he pulls himself up, for one must concentrate on the job in hand. So "but to returne . . ." he says. In other places he is slightly more expansive:

The Black Cherrie or Geen is a Tree I love well . . . there is a sort at Niddrie-castle, where I was born . . . the Fruit is preferable to any Cherrie . . .

Similarly in the last chapter, when he has written, rather sketchily, of hothouses, he explains:

For my part I would rather be in the Woods, Parks, Orchards, Kitchen Garden or fields measuring, planting, and improving the ground.

Reid's claim that he was writing what he himself had never been able to find in manuals is well supported by his text. Intensely aware of the difficulties caused by the "cold, chilled barren Rugged-natur'd ground in Scotland," he had several practical solutions to offer.

First (and last) he urged enclosure: "as there is no countrey can have more need of planting than this, so none more needful of Inclosing".

Second, he was a strong advocate of manuring. (Surely no century has gone more deeply into the properties of various types of dung than did the seventeenth!) He also knew the importance of lime to the generally acid soil of the country.

His third recommendation was to dig thoroughly, using if possible the English spade and double-digging for greatest effect.

Fourthly, he insisted on the benefit of weeding, quoting the "learned Evelyn" but giving us also his own thoughts. "I would advise you to keep them (the kitchen gardens) thus clean of weeds, and if you ever repent it, blame me". It seems strange to us now, but at the time many people believed that weeds kept the ground warm and supplied it with nourishment.

The Scots Gard'ner is divided into two parts. The first treats of planning, surveying, and laying out, the second of cultivation. Part One may at first glance appear dull. Look more closely, and you will see that it contains many good things. Here, for example, you will discover how Reid thought a house should look and be set within its garden:

As the Sun is the centre of this World: as the Heart of the Man is the centre of the man: as the nose the Centre of the face: and as it is unseemly to a Man wanting a leg, ane arme &c. or his nose standing at one side of the face, or not straight, or wanting a cheek, ane eye, ane eare, or with one (or all of them) great at one side and small on the other: Just so with the House-Courts, Avenues, Gardens, Orchards, &c. where regularity or uniformity is not observed.

Observe how totally practical are his methods. Without any equipment save poles, a few sticks, and some string, two or three people could lay out even a large garden to his instructions, achieving perfect regularity and symmetry. We are told how to determine a line when one cannot see its whole length because of hills, woods or houses in the way. As to woods, one of the best methods to run a line through them is to choose a calm night and use candles in lanterns hung on stakes: "let the Candles furthest from you be highest, and remove forward the light as need requires". It is an enchanting concept.

You will not find here revolutionary ideas on layout. Reid follows the fashion of the day in admiring absolute symmetry, with raised beds between straight paths and geometrical figures. He attaches great importance to integrity of design. If an avenue ends in a semicircle, he recommends beginning it with a circle; if it finishes in a triangle it may begin likewise. On the whole he prefers a square garden, with walks leading from the house and no paths running across. And he reminds us that when planting an avenue of trees we should not "mask a fine front, nor veil a pleasant prospect".

He would no doubt be shocked by our modern gardens which use colour and form in the romantic mode, to express or evoke emotion. For the 17th century gardener, regularity and order were symbols of universal laws, all of them discoverable. Therefore, throughout the whole garden, flowers must be planted at equidistant intervals, "and not only so but every sundry colour thereof also; let never two of a kind nor two of a colour stand together without other kinds of colours intervening. . . ." He permits us, however, to use blocks of colour, provided of course that each block is echoed symmetrically.

Part Two concerns cultivation – the care of the soil and plants. We are told how to graft trees, how to prune, how and when to plant, how to wage war against pests and vermin, what seeds to sow, how to accommodate our gardens generally to the Scottish climate.

Notice how, even at that early date, gardeners were importing from other countries. Cauliflower seed comes from Candia (Crete), horse-chestnut seed from Turkey, sweet basil and marjoram "from hotter countries", and the best leek seed is from France. Plants too are imported: "extraordinary clean and smooth barked Elms" can be got from Holland, as can cherries and other stone fruit. It is clear indeed that the Dutch were already in a fair way to becoming garden suppliers to the rest of Europe; Reid recommends not only their plants, but also their mousetraps and their stroups (nozzles) for washing caterpillars off fruit-trees!

Only two varieties of fruit are mentioned by name, the Frontenac grape and the pear called Great Bergamot. Was there then less interest in breeding and selection? The long and detailed instructions for grafting suggest that this is not the case, and we do know from other sources of some early varieties of apple and pear. Fifty years later, a London nurseryman could list dozens of varieties of apple, pear, cherry, peach, apricot, and plum in his catalogue. I cannot help wishing that our Scots Gard'ner had been more forthcoming and specific in his recommendation of fruit for northern climes.

When it comes to vegetables, however, he is detailed enough, and from his book one gets a fair idea of what came to a wealthy man's table. Some items, like scorzonera and samphire, are almost forgotten to-day; others may surprise and even provoke to scepticism. But I have friends who grew fifty pounds of asparagus on an Edinburgh allotment, and I have been told of a family in Orkney who a few years ago "got thoroughly sick" of the huge crop of asparagus they were expected to consume each summer. As for globe artichokes, they are reliably recorded as growing well as far north as Orkney, so Reid's description of them as "a fine and lasting plant" seems justified.

But surely, I hear someone say, the instructions to sow early peas "in the full moon of November" is pure moonshine. Not so. In November 1986 the peas were sown in a garden in Colinton, a suburb of Edinburgh 700 feet above sea level, without protection of any kind. The crop, described as a good one, was ready for eating by the end of May 1987.

The Scots Gard'ner was reprinted once during Reid's lifetime, in 1721. After his death two more editions, "carefully edited . . . by an eminent hand", appeared in 1756 and 1766. As a *vade mecum* for northern gardeners the book continued to be used for many years, only gradually being supplanted by James Justice's *The Scots Gardener's Director*, which had come out in 1754. It then sank into obscurity, whence it was resurrected for brief exposure by A.S. Hyatt's somewhat patronising edition of 1907.

Reid might have difficulty recognising many of the plants, techniques, and tools in use in to-day's gardens; he would certainly be puzzled by Japanese and other influences on design. For us, looking back to him, there is no such bewilderment. His message is as clear and direct as it was three hundred years ago: "by right contrivance . . . you may improve your estates to best advantage, both in Profite and Pleasure". It behoves me now to let him do what he ably can – speak for himself.

Annette Hope
Edinburgh
November 1987

The author extends thanks to Mr. Donald White, Vice-President of the Scottish Genealogy Society, and also to Mr. Ian Milne, of the library of the Royal College of Physicians, for information used in this introduction.

THE
SCOTS GARD'NER

IN TWO PARTS,

The First of Contriving and Planting
GARDENS, ORCHARDS, AVENUES, GROVES:
With new and profitable wayes of Levelling ; and how to
Meafure and Divide Land.

The Second of the Propagation & Improvement of
FORREST, and FRUIT-TREES, KITCHEN-
HEARBES, ROOTS and FRUITS:
With fome *Phyfick Hearbs*, *Shrubs* and *Flowers*.

Appendix fhewing how to ufe the Fruits of the Garden:
Whereunto is annexed

The GARD'NERS KALENDAR.

Publifhed for the Climate of SCOTLAND

By JOHN REID Gard'ner.

Edinburgh, Printed by DAVID LINDSAY, and his
Partners, at the foot of *Heriot's*-Bridge, 1683.

To all the Ingenious

P L A N T E R S

In S C O T L A N D.

I Defire you to perufe this Book, for there are many things in it
of fingular ufe, which I could never find in any, and the fubftance of what I could find material (in the Practical part of Gard'-
nery) improven and applyed home ; whereby I prefume it may be
Satisfactory to you when you operate in the choife of Husbandry.
Several weighty reafons induced me hereunto ; as, the great ne-
ceffity of right contrivance, whereby you may do your works, both
orderly and cheap ; The in-expreffible need of Inclofing and Planting, whereby you may improve your eftates to beft advantage,
both in Profite and Pleafure. And becaufe the many Books on
Gard'nery are for other Countries and Climates, and many things
in them more fpeculative than practical : this enfuing treatife may
the rather be acceptable ; albeit obnoxious to the undoubted cenfure
of Criticks, yet when I reflect on my Innocency in the defign therein (the good of my Country) I receive Encouragment. And that
my Endeavours may prove Succefful, is the earneft defire of

J O H N R E I D.

A 2   T H E

THE
CONTENTS
Of the First Part, which treats of Contrivance.

CHAP. I.

How to make the Works about a House Regular.

CHAP. II.

How to draw by the Scale.

A 3

CHAP.

CHAP. VIII.

How to meafure, divide and lay out Land, &c.

Sect.

THE

THE
CONTENTS

Of the Second Part, which treats of the Culture of Plants.

CHAP. I.

Of the several wayes of Propagation.

CHAP. II.

How to Cultivate and prepare grounds.

B   CHAP.

CHAP. III.

How to propagate and order Forreſt-trees.

CHAP. IV.

Of Hedges or Incloſures.

CHAP. V.

How to propagate and order Fruit-trees:

CHAP.

CHAP. VI.

Of Fruits, Hearbs and Roots for the Kitchen.

Sect.
1. *Of the Fruits of smaller Plants.*
2. *Of Sallads and Pot-hearbs.*
3. *Of sweet Hearbs.*
4. *Of Roots.*
5. *Of Weeding in General.*

CHAP. VII.

Of some Physick Hearbs, Shrubs and Flowers.

1. *Physick Hearbs distinguished into Perennials and Annuals.*
2. *Shrubs distinguished into dry and green.*
3. *Flowers into Fibrous, Bulbous, and Annuals.*
4. *How to preserve the tender sorts in Winter.*

APPENDIX

How to use the Fruits of the Garden.

1. *The manner and season of gathering them.*
2. *How to preserve them when gathered.*
3. *Of their uses.*
4. *How we may have dishes of them.*
5. *How we may have drinks of them.*
6. *To choice their species for our Plantations.*

CON

CONCLUSION

Propoſing Scotland's *Improvement.*

The *GARD'NERS CALENDAR,*

Shewing in each Moneth

When to performe the particulars , &c.
What Garden diſhes and drinks are in ſeaſon.

THE

THE FIRST PART
Treating of Contrivance.

CHAP. I.

How to make the Works about a House Regular.

A First and a Second part I thought necessary, that I might discuss things in their order: for a House must be built before it be furnished. These who inclines not to read this may step foreward to the Second; perhaps there they will find Satisfaction, albeit others may be as desirous of this, who have any works to make.

My designe by contrivance, is to prevent the consequence of Inadvertancy, or the abrupt procedure in Inclosing and Planting.

2. Here in the entrance you may take a view of a House which I have Invented (See Fig. 1.) it is but little, yet very commodious & Cheap. There is only 4 Rooms on a Floor (you may have Closets within the wall, although not here demonstrated) all which enter off the Stayr (yet comunication betwixt) and the door is in the midle, & there is 10 steps up to the first Story, (which is hall or dining Room, withdrawing Room, Bed-Chamber and Waiting-Room) and 10 Steps down to the lower Story, which is half under ground, and vaulted, this is Kitchen, Cellers and Ladners, &c. That above the dining Room story may be Bed-Chambers, library and with-drawing Room: and above these garrets for wardrops. The Roof may be in three so as the midle part may be flat and covered with lead and the two sides more steep & slated: there is also a Stayr coming down

from

from the hall without to the parterre of grafs and gravel, on whofe
corners ar two Pavilions opening without the line of the Houfe and
fets off in place of Iammes ; one of which may be a Store-houfe, and
the other a Dove-houfe : the Stables, Baking and Brewing houfe ar
on the oppofite fide, moft conveniently placed, as hereafter I fhall
demonftrate.

3. Situate your Houfe in a healthy Soyl, near to a frefh-fpring, de-
fended from the Impetuous-weftwinds, northern colds and eaftern
blafts : and mind regularity, *viz.*

Make all the Buildings and Plantings ly fo about the Houfe, as
that the Houfe may be the Centre; all the Walks, Trees and Hedges
running to the Houfe.

As the Sun is the Centre of this World : as the Heart of the man
is the Centre of the man : as the nofe the Centre of the face : and
as it is unfeemly to fee a Man wanting a leg, ane arme &c. or his nofe
ftanding at one fide the face, or not ftreight, or wanting a cheek,
ane eye, ane eare, or with one (or all of them) great at one fide and
fmall on the other; Juft fo with the Houfe-courts, Avenues, Gardens, Orchards, &c. where regularity or uniformity is not obferved.

Therefore whatever you have on the one hand, make as much,
and of the fame forme and in the fame place, on the other.

4. But if you would work right, beginne orderly, that is, find the
central line by erecting a perpendicular on the midle of the Houfe-
front, to extend as farr both back and fore as requifite : hence you
may draw parallels, Meafure and Stake out your Avenues, Gardens,
&c. as you pleafe : ever minding to Meafure alike at both fides of
the Central line; How to find this Central line and to fet off parallels is taught in Chap : 3 : Sect : 1. and 2.

5. Yet for further Illuftration take ane example by a draught of
my own inventing (fee fig : 2.) which if rightly underftood may
be applyed diverfly and Improven elegantly.

It is here in a fmall Scale. the Houfe is in the Centre, and at B,
round by the Houfe is Balefters, the Common Avenue is by N,
and

and ends in a triangle,   *c*, is the outer Court, and in the two triangular Courts marked with O, ar placed the office-houses most
notably (with their back part to the Court *c*,) opening without
the line of the House : So dismounting at the gate of the Court
(through which you may walk on foot to the House) let the Horses
be taken about to the Stables by the Way the ending of the Avenue
leads. The two plots P, may be Pondes, the two with G, Cherrie Gardens : a proper place also for goosberries, Currans, and
Straberries. On the south side the House there is the pleasure or
Flower-Garden called the *Parterre*, at the two sydes thereof Kit-
chen-Gardens marked with K, then another Walk ending in a Semicircle at S, Leading out to the Lawn or deer Park. The vistaes
or walks of view that runs from the 4 Angles of the House ar very
pleasant and convenient, and ar good Shelter ; for which cause there
ar two Thickets on the north side marked with *t*, on the south
side are two such marked *a*, for Nurseries, and at E, and W, ar two
Orchards.   The whole is environed with two rowes of Forrest
Trees without the wall : And if the paper were large I would shew
you that the Park Wall should be parallel to these, that is, every
where equidistant from the House its Centre at least, the whole an
octagone near to a regular *polygon* consisting of equal sides & Angles.
The walks with their fences (being run foreward from all the 4 sides
and 4 Angles of the House till they touch at the midle of each side
of the Park Wall,) serves in the Park for divisors: which divisors may
be hawthorn Hedges, and these in the Gardens holly, except the
Court in the entrie and office-house Courts, me thinks walls ar requisite there.   Also there should be ane ascent to the House, (if possible) as at the first Court gate 2 steps, at the 2d 4 steps. &c.   But
Leaving it to let every man apply as his ground and ability will best
admit, I come to speake of regularity, where confined.

    6. But as to work or make regularity among confirments re-
quires Ingenuity ; so is thered ifficulty in teaching the same, because
of the great variety of places : and being that I know not how to give
precepts for it (except what is said above of the Centre and Central
line)

line) therefore I fhall only inftance in by example.

As where I was confined, to add what I will, but to diminifh non. I viewed the works, and found feveral regular and Irregular things don on the one fide the Houfe, and nothing on the other anfwerable: therefore I Staked out the fame on the other ; ftill where I found an Irregular piece on the one fide, I ftaked out the very fame on the o- ther ; and thus two Irregularities produced one uniformity.

Or where there had been much wrought for ane Avenue , but did not Front the Houfe right, by reafon of a precipice on the weft hand. I got on the houfe top, viewed the ground immediatly, faw that I might turn my face towards the Eaft and get ftately Avenues with Gardens on each hand at pleafure, and the faid precipice turned at my back.

But to draw any place firft on Paper, as they ftand, we fee faults plainly , and how to help them accordingly : Therefore to affift you further in making your works orderly I fhall fhew you in the follow- ing Chap.

C H A P. II.

How to draw by the Scale.

All draughts not drawn by the Scale ar but fuppofitions; the Scale makes them ftand directly on Paper as on ground , or would ftand, if put upon it: therefore of fingular ufe in contriving, you fhould have ane eye to the confequence of all your undertakings, left you run Inadvertantly into a fnare: for when you have determined or fet- led on the contrivance, perhaps hath gone a great length in working the fame, yet as you proceed (one thing making way for another) you may come to fee a farr better way, and fo to overturne moft or all that is done, to get your new and better way accomplifhed; which oblidges you either to double pains & Charges, or otherwife, in fay- ing the fame, to fit ftill with a diffatiffied mind; all which may be eafi- ly and timely prevented by drawing & projecting on paper, as is faid.

2. You

2. You may make as many Scales as you think will be needful, infomuch that when you have a draught at any time to draw, you have no more to do, but by Arithmetick find which of them Scales you muft draw it by. Therefore make a Thinn broad rule 2 foot long Pear or Aple tree, Red of Plumtree, Planetree, Boxwood, or Brafs which is beft : put as many on bothfides as it will contain. I make moft ufe of a Diagonal Scale, (fee fig. 3.) its done by dividing the Inch into fo many equal parts, as 8 in the Inch, 30 in the Inch, 100 or 200 in the Inch, the figure and Multiplication will informe you for 5 divifions drawn the length of the Rule and 7 in the Inch; the other way is a Scale of 35 in the Inch, 5 times 7 is 35 and fo furth. If your Rule be 2 foot, there may be 2 Lengthes on it, or as your largeft Compafs may conveniently reach. You may alfo make fome of the common Scales, that is, divide the Inch the ordinary way in a ftraight line into fo many equal parts (fee fig. 4.) feeing the Diagonals hath only fuch as Multiplication produceth.

3. If you be to draw a draught, but knows not how to take your meafures from the Scale, then if you know the meafures on ground take fo many divifions (off the Scale with your Compafs) as you had feet, ells, or falls (whatever you meafure by) and fet on the Paper: example, if you were to draw an orchard whofe lenth is 680 ells by a Scale of 200 in the Inch (as the upper end of *fig.*3.) you are to confider how many times 200 is in 680, that fo many whole Inches you may take on your Compafs, and the odds or fraction you may get therewith from the fubdivided Inch : here if you fet one foot of the Compafs at 6 and reach the other to *a*, which 6 half Inches is 600, and 8 divifions foreward on the fubdivided half Inch is 80; the fame you may place on the Paper & draw accordingly. Example 2. by the other Scale of 100 in the Inch, if you would fet the breadth of 23 foot-walk on Paper, here it is not one Inch, therefore you muft take but fuch a part of one Inch, *viz.* Set the Compafs from *a*, at the end of the fubdivided half Inch to *o* in the fame, and thus it is on the Compafs; therefore do as before. You may perceive that the 23 divifions on the Rule is the 3 from 20 foreward on the line betwixt 20

C   and

and 3 o where the *o* is placed to make it plain.　If your draught be fo large that your Compafs cannot reach its length, then you may divide the fame by 2, 3, or 4, &c. and take the product on the Compafs and fet alongft fo many times as was your divifor.　This is fo plain that it needs no exemple.

4.　But if you have a draught to draw on one or many fheets of Paper, and you defire to draw it as large as the Paper will bear, not to go off; Then take the length of your Paper in Inches, by which divide the length of your ground whether feet, ells, &c. and the quotient fhall be the Scale you muft draw it by; that is, an inche divided into fo many equal parts.　Example, if you have a plot 360 foot in length to draw on a fheet common Paper 16 Inches: but to make it, keep a little within the Paper, at each end call it 15 inches; fo 360 the length of the ground divided by 15 the length of the Paper gives 24: therefore take a Scale of 24 in the inche, and draw it by the fame. Example 2. the breadth of a field 864 Falls, I defire to draw it on the ⅛ of a fheet *viz.* 3 Inches.　Divide 864 by 3, it gives 288, but this being too fmall, I take the ½ thereof *viz.* 144 and drawes it by the fame, mynding that each divifion on my Paper is 2 Falls on ground.

5.　Or if you had a draught, and knowes not what Scale it was drawn by, if you know what ground it contains, the work is firft, to meafure it by a fuppofed Scale, and fecondly to find a mean proportional betwixt the true quantity of Acres and that quantity found by the fuppofed Scale.　And thirdly by the golden Rule fay, as the quantity of Acres found by the fuppofed Scale is to the mean proportional: fo is the fuppofed fcale to the true Scale.　Example, if you have a plot or field of ground containing 72 Acres, and you meafure it by a Scale of 18 Falls in the inche, and that makes but 40½ Acres, the queftion is what Scale was it drawn by?　You will find the mean proportional betwixt 40. 5. and 72 to be 54 (as in chap. 8. fect. 6.) and as 40. 5. is to 54: fo is 18 to 24. Thus it appears that the faid plot was drawn by a Scale of 24 Falls in the inche.

Exam-

Example 2. If you have a plot (containing 1 4 Acres 64 falls, and meafuring it by a Scale of 40 in the inche makes 90 Acres, what Scale was it drawn by? You will find (as is faid) the mean betwixt 14· 4. and 90 to be 3 6 : therefore as 90 the Acres found by the fuppofed Scale, is to 3 6 the mean proportional : fo is 40 the fuppofed Scale to 1 6 the true Scale. This tells that it was drawen by a Scale of 1 6 in the Inche.

6. But if you have a draught, and knowes not what Scale it was drawn by nor what ground it containes, fo as thereby you might find its Scale, & you defire to diminifh or Enlarge the fame on Paper, and yet that it may bear the fame fhape and proportion in every refpect.

You may divide or multiply every particular line or part of it : as if you would have it ⅓ lefs, then divide each part by 3, and take one of thefe and fet on the Paper. Or if you would have it twice as large, then double every part and portion of it, that is, take the double of each length and breadth on the Compafs and fet on the Paper and draw accordingly.

But if your draught be a Taliduce, Mapps, or the like, draw a fquair by the outter edg thereof, and divide each fide into fo many equal parts, as you think fit; betwixt which draw parallel lines all through crofsing from oppofite fides, and notice what part of your draught falls within the precinct of each little fquair, & fo Copy it upon another Paper whether larger or lefser, as if you would have it one fifth lefs , take one fifth of the fide of one of the little fquairs, and therewith Lottrie or fquare your clean Paper. And likewayes take one fifth of length and breadth of each particular within each little fquair, and the one fifth diftance that fuch and fuch parts, creeks and angles are diftant from any two of the angles of the fame; and fo place them accordingly in the lefser little fquairs of your clean Paper.

7. When you defigne to furvey any plot of ground be careful in meafuring the diftances truly, and keep exact accompt thereof. You may make firft a fuppofed figure on a Paper before you begin, that thereon you may write your meafures, as you go along : as if it be a

C 2   Hexa-

Hexagon, *(fee fig. 27.)* draw a figure at random containing 6 fides, and having obferved the meridian on the ground (which you may either find by the Compafs or let the central line of the Houfe its perpendiculars or parallels ferve in lieu thereof *)* mark down fuch on your fuppofed figure : then let the two men with the chain begin at any angle ; the foremoft may have 10 fmall fticks to thruft in at every length of the chain, & let the hindermoft man gather them up as he comes along; and when all up, give them to his affiftant to begin again, as before, calling that, one change (ftill being carefull to go ftraight betwixt the two ends or extreams) and when you come at the other end, compt how many changes, chaines, and links, as if the hedg *c. d.* be 70 Falls, write that down as in the figure, and fo proceed to the reft obferving the fame methode.

8. But albeit you meafure round any plot or Field, yet you muft know how to find the quantity of the angles, and protract the fame : therefore I fhall fhew you the moft exact of all others and mechanical too. Example by *fig.* 21. When you have meafured the length of the 4 fides of this Trapezia (as is taught) then meafure alfo betwixt any of the two oppofite angles, as from *c.* to *b.* or from *d.* to *a.* and then you may protract it only with your Scale thus : draw a given line on the Paper as *a. c.* and from your Scale take fo many divifions as was the lenth of the hedg *a .c.* and fet thereon ; and take the lenth betwixt *c.* and *b.* on your Compafs ; fet one foot in *c.* and difcribe an obfcure Arch at *b.* alfo take the lenth of *a. b.* and fetting one foot in *a* make another Arch to crofs the former at *b.* then draw the line *a. b.* likewayes take the length of the fide *b. d.* on the Compafs, fet one foot in *b.* difcribe an obfcure arch at *d.* and take the length *c. d.* & with one foot in *c.* crofs the former at *d.* then draw *c. d.* and *b d.* and fo have you finifhed. By the fame its eafie to protract *fig.* 26. and 27 or any other, and this is my method of Surveying.

6. As for the dimenfions of Circles, fee Chap : 8. for having the Radius, you may eafily find all things belonging thereunto.

As for ftraight lined figures, if you reduce them into Triangles, & meafure the three fides of each, you may protract them, as is taught:

thus

thus Trigonometry or the doctrine of plane Triangles shewes, that having any three things in a Triangle, we may find the other three, either by the Scale or by Artificial Sines, Tangents, and Logarithims: as having three sides, or three angles, or one Angle, and two sides, or two sides and one Angle, &c.

I will give you ane example by Fig: 20. suppose you would have the distance between B. and A. First measure off from B. (at any side most convenient) so many ells or falls, the more the better, I shall here supose 384 falls to C. (as will appeare by a Scale of 400 in the Inch) and in setting it off, notice what degrees that angle makes by your prorector, then hold the same at C. with its Chord line on B. C. Turn about the Index till it poynt to A. notice what degrees it cutts, as supose 80. and write down: here you have the side B. C. 384. the angle A. B. C. 60. and the angle B. C. A. 80. (and by consequence the Angle B. A. C. 40. being its the complement to 180.) therefore go to your paper and draw a given line as A. B. then open the compass to the radius of your line of Chords, & therewith setting one foot in B. Discribe the Arch D. E. I. O. likwayes take 60 degrees with your Compass off the line of Chords, & set from D. to E. on that Arch line, and by the poynt. B. and E. draw the line B. E. C. so shall the Angle. A. B. C contain 90. degrees. But if the Angle had fallen to be more than 90 degrees, then you may take it at twice (seeing the ordinary line of Chords has but 90) as if the Index had Cut 120. first take 90 upon the compass and set from. D. to I. then take 30 and set from. I. to O. which Angle. A. B. O. contains 120 degrees. But to return, as you set off the Angle at. B. so likewayes at the Angle. C. make an Arch and set off 80 degrees thereon, by which poynt and C. Draw the line. C. A. lastly take the line B. A. on your compass (i. e. betwixt the poynt. B. and the poynt at. A. where the line. C. A. did cut the line. B. A.) and apply to the same Scale of 400 in the Inch, from whence you tooke the 384. and you will find the distance betwixt B. and A. to be 588 Falls: for,

As

As the Sine of the Angle B. A. C. 40 degrees . .   9: 808067
is to the Logarithm of the fide B. C. 384 falls: . . .   584331
fo is the Sine of the Angle B. C. A. 80 degrees . .   9: 993351
    The fumme of the 2d. and 3d. added   · . 10: 577682
    The firft number to be fubftr: from this fum   9: 808067
To the Logarithm of the fide A. B. 588 falls . . .   769625

If you would know how to find the fuperficial content of any
plot of ground, or how to divide the fame, or to lay out any quantity
of land in whàt forme foever, &c. fee Chap: 8. for, I haft to.

CHAP. III.

How to make Avenues and Walkes.

ALL walkes fhould front the gates or entries, whether they lead
to a houfe, Garden, Gate. Door, Park, Wood, or highway.
When you have determined on the end of the walk as the door of the
houfe, in the midle thereof on the line of the Houfe-front fet off a
perpendicular, to find the central line as aforefaid, fee Chap. 1. Sect.
4. and for your more exact performance thereof prepare this Inftrument, *viz.* take two ftraight Rules about 3 or 4 foot long, joyn them
Crofswayes in other, fo that the 4 Angles where they cutt may be
exact fquairs; then at each end of thefe, joyn a piece Rule ftanding
up about 4 or 5 Inches, and in the exact midle of each of thefe pieces
make a flit up and down, and in the midle of thefe flits a piece fmall
filk threed; thefe being ftraight and perpend : up are excellent to
view by. Place this crofs on the head of the three footed Staff, hing
a Plumb whereby you may plant it Horizontale upon occafion : on
this you may alfo place your prorector with the box and needle,
when you go to furveying, for every one has not a plane Table.

As

As to the Avenue, set one side of your cross parallel to the given line (the House-wall) this you may do with most ease, by taking one end thereof within the door till the side touch the door cheeks; and you may also view cross by the side-wall backsight and foresight, till it stand exactly Parellel thereto : then turne, and standing within the door, view straight out by the silk threeds, and so direct one to drive stakes all along so farr as you can see, in a straight and perpend: line. You may also find this perpendicular central line, thô Walls, Hedges, Houses, Trees &c. obstruct, if you can see over them out at any Window or off the Battlement if there be any, otherwayes recurre to the Rules in Sect. 3. and 4.

And as by this Instrument you may raise any perpendicular, so by the same you may let perpend fall : for you may alter it hither and thither upon the given line, till it direct to the angle or point assigned.

2. The mid or central line of your Avenue being found out you must place your cross thereon, and thereby set off the half breadth thereof at each side : do this at both ends and midle, that they be exactly Parallel; and therein drive stakes almost to the head. And when you come to marke out for the Trees, or to plant them, set a straight pole at each driven stake, for your direction in going straight betwixt the same.

If the length of the walke be confin'd, divide it by the distance you mynd to plant at; and if there be any odd, add or substract till all the distances be equal : which distance you must take on a chain (for a line will reach and shrink) and begin at one end, and go straight to the other, thrusting in a small stake at each length; minding to let both rowes go on squair together, that is, one on each side and viewing will find the other two, if there be fower rowes, see the Avenues fig. 2.

And though the ground be unevenly, yet you must hold the chain level : wherefore you may have a squair & Plumb fixed at your pole or staff for your more exact performance thereof.

When

When you have staked out the ground, prepare the rounding string *viz.* a piece line doubled and tyed near the point of a stick, and so put the double on the stakes where the Trees must stand, and streatching the same, make a scratch with the point of the stick round, and with a spade follow that Compass and make the hole. See the second part of this Treatise, where there be directions how to prepare the ground and plant.

If you observe what is said, you may stake out any kind of walk, having one line found; wherefore I shall shew you how to find out one line whatever obstruct.

3. As first, suppose you would run a line or walke through a wood: when you have concluded on the end thereof, there erect a perpendicular as above, and run it as farr into the wood as you can; then at each side thereof set off a Parallel line two or three foot from the central line, or half the breadth of the intended walk: so shall you have three Parallel lines running on in straight lines together. And where any one runns on a tree, run foreward the other two, and set it off again (when past the Tree) as it was Parallel to its fellowes, and so proceed till you be through the wood, or thickets, still marking the Trees that falls in the intervall to be cut.

A second way is by means of Lanthornes with burning Candles, in a calm night when dark hanged on stakes, you standing in the wood may plant stakes at pleasure, let the Candles furthest from you be highest, and remove foreward the lights as need requires.

4. But if both ends of your walk be determined, and you cannot see betwixt, by reason of Lengthes, Hills, Woods, Houses, or some such obstruction, in such a case let two having each a pole go to the midle or to such a place betwixt where they may (by looking backsight and foresight) perceive the two extreams, (where should be a pole with white Paper on the slip boards to make the better appearance) turn your faces towards other, standing at a large distance asunder, but so as you may both see your respective objects. And let A direct B to set the pole in line with his and that at the North-end: and B direct A to hold in line with his and that at the South-end:

end: so each directing other by words or Signes; let both alter to and fro, till they have their desires at once; then shall these two and the extreams be all four in a straight line, whereby you may set as many as you please. This way I found out by experiment, and thinks it worthy a place amongst the Mathematicks.

But if you cannot see the two ends, when standing in the midle; although the Poles be never so high, then if it be Wood or Hedges, the foresaid Lanthrons and Candles will do the businefs.

But if the obstructions be Hills, Walls, or Houses, for which you cannot see, standing in the midle, as a-foresaid, neither by Lanthrons, nor yet by high Poles; then do by Parallels thus: set off a parallel line so farr,as that it may run quyt beyond the obstruction, (on the side most convenient) then set in the parallel again at convenient places; so shall both agree, and as will appear when the obstruction is removed.

But if none of these will do, run a line over by guefs, and if it mifs (as no wonder) take notice of your Errour at the end, by letting a perpendicular fall on the determined poynt (by means of the squair or crofs) and the meafure betwixt finds out the Errour: then meafure the length of your intended walk or line, aforefaid; and at the quarter thereof, set off the $\frac{1}{4}$ of your Errour: At the midle the $\frac{1}{2}$ and at the $\frac{3}{4}$ of the length, set off the $\frac{3}{4}$ of your Errour; this will lead you straight upon your purpofe.

Trigonometry will alfo folve this, if you could work exactly: for here you have two sides and one angle; fee the laft Chap. Sect. 9.

5. And if you have a given line and desires to set of a Parallel therefrom, but cannot meafure off at both ends as is needfull, there being Trees, Waters, Hills, Walls or Houses, obstructing, you may meafure, fquair or Perpendicular off at any part of the given line (that is moft convenient)fo far as you mind to go with your parallel; at, or upon which point erect another Perpendicular to run back-

fight and forefight; the which shall be exactly parallel to the given line, as was required.

6. Having given some directions for staking out walks for Planting, yet your Avenues and Walks must end in some figure or another, whether Triangular, Circular, Ovall, &c. For Coaches and Carts to turn in, as also where Walks meets, or Cross other, its requisite that there be some figure for the same reason.

How Avenues may end in Semicircles and Triangles, see fig : 2. and if it end in a Semicircle, it may begin with the same or rather (if the ground will suffer) it should begin with a whole circle having fower opposite opens the breadth of the walk : If it end with a Triangle, it may begin so likwayes, but rather with a squair (the endings Integer) whose entries or opens must be in its Angles. And also where the Walkes meets or Cross, I have a little figure or Open, see fig : 2. And yet the Trees in the whole draught every way lineal, except in the segment of a Circle, where they deviat a little. The figures should be at least three times the breadth of the walk, but so as the ground will admit; let not the Trees in the figure stand much above half the distance of these in the walke, but divide equally. make the breadth of the walk in proportion to its length : I think an Avenue a mile in length may be 40 ells in breadth, see Chap : 5. sect : 2. neither short Broad nor long narrow walkes are handsome, except in case of walkes of Shade, & also of Avenues where the Front of the house, Jammes, courts, or pavilions ar to be observed: for the breadth of the court should be at least the whole length of the House-front; & if two Jammes the midle walke of the Avenue may be the breadth betwixt, and the side-walkes the breadth of the Jammes; or the mid walk the breadth of the whole Front, & the side walkes the breadth of the pavilions, which ar on the corners of the Court; or divide the House-Front in three, making the midle walke the just breadth of both the side ones: so shall they be every way lineall, but do not mask a fine Front nor veyle a pleasant prospect. The length of the Avenue, it should run so farr as (when we stand at the house) we may lose sight of the farr end, if possible. When it runs over a Brac, then

to

to the eye it appears *Infinitum*, and where that cannot be had, it doth very well where the fight terminates in a grove or circle of Firrs.

7. The diftance of Trees is fometimes according to the quality of the ground, or Trees to be planted, fomtimes to the number of Rowes, or as the figure to be planted will beft admit. If a good Soyl, plant at the wider diftance ; if 4 Rowes, as an Avenue, Plant at 5. 6. 7. or 8 ells diftance ; if 2 fingle rowes at 4. 5. or 6 ells ; if circular figures or the like at 2, 3 or 4 ells, or as the figure is in fmall-nefs or greatnefs, and Plant fo as they may fhew the figure well.

Some Trees requires wider diftance than others, thefe that grow greateft, by confequence muft have the largeft diftance, fee the next Chap : fect : 10.

Note, that you Intermix not great Trees and fmall Trees in Plan-ting, neither quick-growers and flow-growers : for I obferve a kind of Emulation amongft them.

For Inclofures See part 2. Chap : 4.

C H A P. IIII.

How to Plant Thickets and Orchards.

AS the ground where you Plant muft be Inclofed, fo muft the Trees ftand fome diftance off the fence : if it be a wall where-on ar Wall-Trees, let the ftandards be at leaft one of their own dif-tances from the fame, & if you defigne fine walks round by the wall, Plant the Row next thereunto with Dwarff-Trees or fome low Hedge, and the Trees half a diftance off fuch ; if the inclofure be a Hedge, obferve the fame Rule. Alfo let the Trees be Parallel to the Inclofure : but every Plot will not fuffer to be Planted every way lineal and ftand Parallel to the Inclofure too ; therefore it will be neceffary firft to Inquire a little what figures they be that may

thus

thus be Planted, (a thing I never faw Inquired) And fecondly how to plant thofe that will not admit of this order, and laftly how to plant the feveral wayes.

2. The figures that may be planted every way in row ar many,yet forBrévities fake I fhall mention but fome as oblong , & geometrical fquairs (fee fig: 5. 6. 7. 8. 9.) Rhombus (fee fig:10.) Rhomboïdes (fee fig. 11.) Oxigone or Equilateral Triangle (fee fig : 12.) Orthygone or right Angled Triangle (fee fig : 13.) Ambligone or Triangle with one obtufe and two Acute Angles, (fee fig: 14.) a fort of Trapezia, (fee fig : 15.) Hexagone, (fee fig:16.) Octagone (as the whole fig: 2.) thefe regular Polygones ar the neareft way for Planting a Circle.

Many more figures there be both Regular and Irregular that will admit of this order, but thefe may fuffice for Illuftration. As for thefe that will not, you may Plant them Parallel , to as many fides as you can , and let the reft, fall as they will.

3. Now as to the feveral wayes fo farr as I know, there is but three principal wayes of Planting , every way lineal (although there be more built thereon) *viz.* Squair, Rhombus,and Triangle : In the firft, three of them makes a right Triangle, and fower of them difcribes a Circle ; (fee Fig: 5.) In the fecond, three of them makes a triacute Triangle,and fower of them difcribes an Elipfis (fee fig: 6.) note, that this way will admit of Variation. In the third , three of them makes an equilateral Triangle, and fower of them difcribes an Ovall, (See Fig: 7.) And feven of them makes a Circle with a Centre, See Fig: 17.

4. The manner of Planting the firft, which is the common way is exemplified in Fig: 5. take the length of one fidé, and divide by the diftance you mind to plant at, and the product tells how many, and whats over,if there be any,you may proportion as before. Then with your determined diftance on a chain, begin at a Corner and go round the out-line exactly, where the outter row muft ftand, thrufting in a ftake at every length ; thefe being in ftraight line and at equall diftances, alfo ftraight bodyed and perpendicular up. The way is thus : One muft ftand at W. and view to E. another at S.

and

and view to N. Caufing a thrid fet a Stake in line with both as at L.
So removing from Stake to Stake (viewing ftill to the oppofite) direct the thrid by words or fignes till his Stake be in line with both:
thus proceed till all the plot be Staked out. See Fig. 5. The way
the Trees will ftand when Planted.

But if the ground be unevenly, caufe the Stake-fetter, hold up a
long and ftraight pole (with a plumb Rule for holding it perpend:)
and when he removes, to thruft a ftake exactly where the pole ftood:
but if the pole will not do, let the viewers mount them on three footed or ftanding leathers; and if that will not do, betake to the Rule,
mentioned in the laft Chap, for taking a line over a Hill, where both
ends ar confined, as I have done, in the like cafe.

But becaufe fome fcarcely knowes fignes, the Stake-fetter muft be
told that when the viewer ftands his face northwards and waves the
right hand Eaftward, that he muft go a little eaft with his Pole,
and when he waves the left, then weftwards, when both his hands at
once eaft or weft, then he muft hold the head of the Pole (if he have
no plumb for his direction in this) but when the viewer moves both
Hands, or Hat, up and down, then the Stake-fetter muft fix
there.

5. If you Plant the fecond way in a fquair, the out-line round is
not equal diftances thô the oppofites fide are; here in this example
one fide is about 12 and one half ells diftance, and the other 15. and
the viewing being Angular, and not from oppofite fides makes the
Trees ftand about 10 and one half ells.

But if you will Plant Rombufoical, as is defigned, then its don by
the equal divifion of its fower fides, and by viewing to its oppofits,
as the Rombus A. B. C. D. Within Fig: 6. Doth reprefent; for
though its Angles be not fquair nor equal, yet its fides muft be e-
qual, and Angles oppofite: and here it may be varyed, as is faid according to the fhape of the ground, by ftreatching longer or opening
it wider. A. C. is its breadth and D. B. its length. Or you may alfo
plant by the Romboides, as I have done, D. A. E. F. & confequently
many more figures may be planted thereby as well as thefe may be,

varyed

varyed or altered, and yet all continue in this *Cyrus* order.

6. In the 3d way take an example in Fig: 7. where the length of one side must be divided by the determined distance *viz*. the distance off the fence being substracted, the length of the side A. B. is 1 1 9 and I designe to plant at 8 and ane half ells: therefore I divide 1 1 9 by 8. 5. decimally, the product is 1 4 distances; then there will be 1 5 rowes; here one side is Staked out, whereby you may Plant the whole plot thus: take two distances on the chain, that is, hold one end exactly at A. And the other at C. Again with that measure on the Chain, hold one end at the first Stake (*viz*: A.) And the other at the second (*viz*: L.) cause a thrid take the chain by the exact midle, and (holding it stiff) thrust in a straight stake at the Angle of the Chain (*viz*: N.) so those three makes an equilateral Triangle; then remove, holding one end at the second Stake (*viz*: L.) And the other at the thrid *viz*. C. Streatch the Chain and thrust in a Stake at its Angle or midle as before. Thus you may proceed from Stake to Stake till that row be Planted: and so on from row to Row till the whole Plot be Staked out, minding to set the Stakes straight and Perpendicular, considering their thicknefs also; in all which if you be not very exact, ye cannot avoyd error before you come at the other side. Therefore I shall shew you another way of my own Inventing, which is more sure and exact & lefs paines, *viz*: Let first that one side be marked out, as before, and having set two or three Stakes of the second row, as is juft now taught; then upon two, hold to the Chain, and Plant another Stake to begin a thrid row; (as at D.) then take the exact distance betwixt L. and D. On the Chain, and therewith Stake out the side B. R. And becaufe there is one Odd Row, take the exact half of that distance (by doubling the Chain)& set from R. to L. then with the whole length go betwixt B. L. thrusting in a Stake at each length, and here you shall find three distances and the half that was set off at the Angle R. Thus two sides ar Staked out, and he that can do this, can also Stake out the other two, seeing the opposite sides are answerable: for as A. B. is to H. L. so is L. B. unto H. A.

When the plot is staked out round, let one stand at X, and view to B. & another at O. and view to R. cause a third, set a stake in line with both, as at Q. Thus you may proceed from stake to stake, till all the plot be marked out, still minding the way of your viewing.

A Plot will contain more Trees this way, than any other example. The two Plots, fig. 5. and 7. are both alike in shape and quantity, each containing one Acre, 2 Roods, 16 Falls, 30 Ells: and fig. 7. holds 11 Trees more than fig. 5. planted at one and the same distance.

7. A fourth way of planting, is that which I ordinarly use in thickets: (see fig. 8) for when the Trees growes large, every other row (suppose the short ones) may be taken out, that the rest may have freedom, and so be benifited by Sun and Air, where one Fruit-tree will bear more than fower crouded on others, and yet continue in as good order; and in part answers some complaining while their Orchards are young, as having few Fruit, seeing the more Trees there be while such, the more fruit to be expected, therefore when their branches begin to meet, remove them as is said, lop and plant by your Hedges, I mean by the divisors of your Corn Land, and they being now great, are able to defend themselves. Its also applicable to Forrest-trees seeing while they are young, they afford little Shelter, except more than ordinary thick, and yet when they grow large cannot prosper to that stately magnitude, unless the same cure be used, *viz.* the removal of each second row, which may be effectually planted about the Bordures of your Corn Land, Medow and Pasture, who now needs no fence save a few thorns hanged about to keep the Cattle from Rubbing, which thornes they are now well able to bear, albeit small Trees are not: for the winds take great hold on such. Moreover in Orchards, if the short Rowes be Cherries and Plumes, they not being long lived, will be past their best e'r the Aples and Pears (which may be in the long rowes) require their Room from them.

As to the methode you must mark out the plot round about, as in my first, and view from Angle to Angle of each Geometrical squair;

but

but then the diftance of the outter Row about, muft be more than in the firft way, otherwife the Trees will ftand much nearer. As 7. is to 5. fo is the diftance of the outter row about to the diftance of the Trees through the Plot.

Or you may plant it by viewing from oppofite fides, as in my firft way, only you muft plant the out-line of ftakes round about, at half the former diftance, and let the Stake-fetter pafs by every other diftance (except you mean to plant Goosberries, and Curran-Standards in thefe blanks, and then the Trees and Shrubs together makes it Intirely one with the firft way,) and now the proportion is, as 7 is to 10 : fo is the diftance of the outter row about, to the diftance of the Trees; or as 10 is to 7 : fo the diftance of the Trees to the diftance of the outter row about. Such proportion doth the fide, and diagonal of a Geometrical fquair, bear the one unto the other exact enough for our purpofe.

8. The fifth way, and very notable, where Orchard and Kitchen Garden are all one, or where you have Corn or Grafs amongft your Trees, or Trees (whither barren or Fruit) among your Corn or Grafs. (*fee fig.* 9.)

If for Kitchen Garden, divide it in Ridges, making the Tables or Pathes in the midle of the wideft Intervall, and then fubdivide fo as the Trees may fall in the midle of the Beds, or Bordures. If for Corn-land, the ridg muft be between each row, plowed within fower foot on each fide the rowes or ranges of Trees : which eight foot Bordures muft be delved each fpring; or if ftiff clay, at both equinoxes, and no vegitable fuffered to grow thereon. For a man or two with large and handfome hawes 10 Inches broad, will quickly go through them in Summer, and cut the weeds at their firft peeping: this would certainly be a great Improvement; and whither you apply to Corn or Grafs, Fruit or Forreft-trees, I would advife you to keep them thus clean of weeds, and if ever you repent it, blame me.

9. A fixt way of planting Trees is, to make all the walkes or In-tervalls open from the Houfe proportionally, fo as when you

ſtand at the Houſe, the walkes may appear all of an equal breadth to the eye, this would ſuit well with my contrivance of the Houſe, being like the Sun ſending forth his beams.

10. The diſtance of Trees in Thickets and Orchards, is either according to the quality of the ground, Trees to be planted, or methode of planting.

If a good and deep ſoil, there Trees will live long and grow great and requires a large diſtance: Apples planted the 1ſt., 2d., and 3d., way may be from 8 to 10 ells diſtance : Pears ſo planted at 10 or 12 Ells, and of theſe planted the 4th. way may be at the leaſt diſtance mentioned, becauſe they will ſtand near the greateſt when every ſecond is removed; but if planted the 5th. way they may be from 16 to 20 Ells one way, and from 8 to 10 the other : Cherries and Plumes from 5 to 7 Ells being planted the 1ſt., 2d., 3d., or 4th. way; as for the diſtance of dwarfs and Wall-trees, ſee the next Chap. Sect. 5.

At the Pears diſtance plant Oak, Elm, Aſh, Plan, Beach, Wallnut, Cheſnut; at the Aples diſtance plant Geens, Service, Lines, Poplars; at the diſtance of Plum and Cherrie plant Maple, Hornbeam, Haſſell, Birch, Laburnum, Aſpen, Aſder, Willowes, Pin, Firr, Yew. And ſee the laſt Chap. Sect. 7. for more directions.

If the ground be level, plant ſuch Trees as grow loweſt, at the South-ſide, and ſtill higher by degrees towards the North, that the taleſt and ſtrongeſt may be on the North-ſide; ſo ſhall the Northren blaſts be guarded off, and the Sun-beames the better received in amongſt them. If the ground be not level, plant ſuch as grow low, on the higheſt ground, and the contrary. And ſet alwayes the crooked or leaning ſide, towards the Southweſt; whence comēs the greateſt winds, which in few years will make them the more erect : for you may ſee that all Trees that are not well ſheltered from theſe Weſterly winds, leans or declines therefrom.

When the ground is all marked out with ſtakes, put on the roundig ſtring, and make the holes. See the laſt Chap. Sect. 7. I uſe

not

not to make them lefs than 6 foot Diameter for ordinary Trees, and you may fuffer the outter row of ftakes to ftand, till you plant the reft that you may view thereby.

How to order the ground, and plant, fee the fecond part of this Book ; and for Inclofures fee the fame fecond part, Chap. 4.

CHAP. V.

How to make the Kitchen Garden.

THE Kitchen-Garden is the beft of all Gardens, but to returne. In all Gardens it is ordinary firft to make a Bordure at the Wall. Secondly a walke. And thridly a Bordure on the other fide thereof; here, the walke with a Bordure on each fide of it, going round the whole plot, Parallel to the Wall : but if your ground be large enough, I bid you make a diftance Intercept betwixt the walk and the Wall. Its alfo ordinary to divide the Garden into four plots, by two walkes crofling from fide to fide : but I am not for any crofs walkes in Gardens; yet if you would have more than one, (which divides the whole into two parts) then make them all one way through the plot leading to the Houfe, and equidiftant from the midle, ftill making the gates, doors or entries Front the walkes.

In your Kitchen-plots, & in Nurferies for Trees, plant no Trees through the ground : for when they grow up, they cover and choak the ground fo, that you will be neceffitate to feek for another. Therefore, make only three Bordures next and Parallel to the walkes round on each hand : plant the firft or that next the walke on both fides, with a holly Hedg, the fecond with Goosberries and currans, the thrid with dwarff Trees, the ground all open and void within for Kitchen-herbes and Roots; which muft be orderly
divi-

divided into ridges; and thefe again divided into Beds, Furrowes, and Drills for your more orderly and convenient planting and fow-ing. As for the proportion note that.

2. The walkes muft be in breadth according to their length *viz.* 1000 foot long, 30 foot broad, 500 foot long, 20 foot broad, 250 in length, 15 in breadth, 100 foot long, 10 foot broad.

The Bordures 6 foot broad, the Tables or Pathes betwixt the Bordures 2 foot broad, and thefe betwixt the level-Ridges (where-in the ground is divided) 3 foot broad, the Beds 6 foot broad with foot and half furrowes; you may make 7 of them Beds in each Ridg, and the whole length of the plot all Running from the Houfe: but if your ground be fmall you may make your Bordures and Beds nar-rower, yet ftill let the whole plot, Ridges, Bordures, and Beds be equally divided, and their Areas or Edges three Inches higher than the furrows or pathes, and fo much higher than the fide of walkes, as the middle of the walk is higher than its fides, all hand-fomly clapt up with the Rakehead, by a line: (and the like order you may obferve in your feminaries and Nurferies of Trees) then plant and fow by lines and Drills, both for beauty and conve-niency.

When you would do this, divide the Bed, Bordure or Ridg at both ends into fo many equal parts: (by help of the long Rule and fmall fticks) then ftreatch on the line from end to end by thefe fticks, and with the corner of the Rule make a marke by the line; and therein fet your Herbes and Plants; and for fetting of feeds, meafure out, and ftreatch on the line as before, and with the fetting ftick make the holes by the line (not too deep) and therein put the feeds. And if you fow in drills, make a fcratch or little ebb gutter with the point of the ftick by the line, and therein fow. If the rowes be two foot diftance, let the firft be one foot within the edg; if 6 Inches fundry make them 3 Inches off the edge, and fo proportionally Note, that I have told the diftances of each fort Kitchen-herbes and Fruits part 2. Chap. 6. where is intended 6 foot broad beds, but where they are lefs, there muft be fewer rowes.

3. The

3. The Kitchen Garden may be placed, its half on each side the House and Courts, and when you plant or sow, place every species by themselves (except such mixture as is mentioned part 2. Chap. 1. Sect. 3.) and where you have not a whole Ridge or at least a bed of a kind, you may compleat them with such as are nearest of growth and continuance : also plant them of long last, and them that must be yearly renewed severally, each in Ridges or beds by themselves orderly ; the order is to make every sort oppose it self. Example if you plant a Ridge of Artichocks on the one hand, plant another at the same place on the other : and still where you have perennialls on the one side, set the same sort at the same place on the other ; and so of Annualls. In short, what ever you have on the one side, you should have the same in every circumstance on the other. Perennialls are such plants as continues many years in the ground, Annualls are such as usually dy immediatly after once they bear seed, and that is usually (thô not universally) the first or second year.

4. As for physical plot you may have them in that ridge of the Kitchen Garden next the Bordures : and if you will to have no other pleasure Garden, you may have Flowers there, and on the Bordures next the walkes also : and that ridge or Intervall betwixt the walke and Wall will be excellent for all early, rare and tender plants. You may rill your Physick Herbes in Tribes and Kindreds, planting every Tribe by themselves, and you may also place one of each kind in the Alphabetical order.

5. How to order hedges, see part 2. Chap. 4. as for Walls, Brick is best, next is Stone and Lime ; 4 Ells is low enough, 5 or 6 if you please : but if you would make the South-looking Wall semicircles in it, that would conduce much to the advantadge of the Fruit, as well as Hot-beds under it ; The distance of Wall-trees will Informe you what quantity to make them, as for example 15 foot is the distance of Cherries and Plumes, (except such as the *May*-cherrie which being Dwarfish requires less) 18 foot for Apricoks & Peaches, 20 foot for Aples, 24 for Pears. Therefore if you

make

make the femicircumference 18 foot for Apricoks and Peaches, (you may plant two Dwarff Cherries therein) then 36 is the whole Perifery, and as 22 is to 7 : fo is 36 the Perifery to $11\frac{1}{2}$ fere the Diameter; and having the Diameter you may eafily make any part of the Circle : and let the plain or ftraight Wall betwixt each femicircle be juft one Trees diftance likewayes.

And alfo in ftraight Walls divide equally, and plant non in the Corners, meafure firft off 6 foot on each fide the gates or doors for Honifuckles, Jafmines, &c. And whatever be the diftance of your Trees, fet them half therefrom, as alfo from the Corners, except where you make all their heads ply one way; (as on a low Wall) fuch may ftand three foot off the Corners, or Honifuckles they lean from, and a whole diftance off thefe they lean towards. You may plant a Goosberrie and curran in the intervalls of your Wall-trees while young, & when the Trees approach, remove them. Let the Roots of your Wall-trees ftand near a foot from the Wall with their heads inclining towards the fame. Wall-trees in Orchards (whofe Standards are in the Quincunx) fhould ftand oppofite to the mid intervall of the Standards.

The diftance of Dwarff Standards is 16 foot where there is but one row, and in following this Rule of the three Bordures, they will ftand juft 16 foot off the Hedg, obferving to plant in the midle of the Bordures. The diftance of Goosberries and currans 6 foot. But in all your plantings and fowings divide the ground fo as each kind may ftand & grow equally.

To conclude, thefe three Bordures going round at each fide of the walkes handfomly made up and planted, as aforefaid, will fecure the ground within from hurtful winds and colds, and make people keep the walkes (handfome pale doors being on the entries of the Hedges) fo as they may neither wrong you nor themfelves. Alfo the Hedge, Dwarff Standards, Shrubs, and Wall-trees being all well prun'd and plyed, with the Bordures and walkes clean and orderly kept, will make it look like a Garden of pleafure, and hide all the Ruggednefs that happeneth in Kitchen-ground by delving, dunging, turning and overturning throughout the year.

E 3   CHAP.

CHAP. VI.

How to make the pleasure-garden, &c.

PLeasure-Gardens useth to be divided into walkes and plots, with a Bordure round each plot, and at the corner of each, may be a holly or some such train'd up, some Pyramidal, others Spherical, the Trees and Shrubs at the Wall well plyed and prun'd, the Green thereon cut in several Figures, the walkes layed with Gravel, and the plots within with Grass, (in several places whereof may be Flower pots) the Bordures boxed, and planted with variety of Fine Flowers orderly Intermixt, Weeded, Mow'd, Rolled, and kept all clean and handsome.

Plain draughts ar only in use, and most preferable; that which I esteem is plain straight Bordures and Pathes running all one way, that is, from the House with one walke parting it in the midle, leading to the House door : and if the ground be large, you may make one round by the Wall too, as the pleasure-Garden of fig. 1. Let the Bordures and Pathes be both of a breadth, (*viz.* 6 foot) box the Bordures, and plant them with Flowers, lay the pathes as well as the walkes with Gravel, plant the Walls with Fruit and Flower-bearing Trees variously.

Outter Courts hath only one Bordure at the Wall, planted with Laurels and other Greens, one Pathed or Brick-walk in the midle, leading to the midle of the House-front with a long Grass plot on each hand.

2. The Bordures of your Kitchen-Garden round by the walkes may be boxed with *Thyme*, *Lavendar*, *Hysop*, *Rue*, &c. the next with *Parsly*, *Strawberries*, *Violets*, *July-flowers*, &c. Cherrie-gardens and Physick-gardens with Sweet-brier often cut, or *Box* cut three times Per annum as *April*, *June*, *August*, minding to cut their Roots at the inside every second year, that they exhaust not the strength or nourishment of the Flowers or Herbes. But
that

that which I preferre for Flower-Gardens above all, is *Dwarff-Juniper* raifed from the feed and Planted thus, When the ground is levelled, meafure out the Bordures, (but raife them not above the walkes, except you minde to lay gravel) ftreatch a line and with the edge of the Rule mark alongft thereby, and therein fet the young fets of *Box* or the young Plants of *Juniper* at 2 years grouth; then prepare the Bordures by delving in confum'd dung of Cowes and Sheep, covering on a little lime topt with a little fand, to ly all fummer, kept clean from by hawing. At the beginning of winter delve and mix together, to ly all winter un-Raked, and at the Spring redelve, ftirr and mix it throughly, and train and plant your Flowers and other Plants in their feafons. See Part 2. Chap: 7.

3. In making the walkes in any Gardens, firft level up the Bordures at its fides, fecondly drive a Row of Stakes in the midle of the walke, and level them accordingly *i. e.* ftreatch a line crofs the walke betwixt the two level Bordures, and marke where it hits the Stake in the midle of the walke; do this at both ends, and viewing betwixt, will levell the reft, fee the next Chap: of levelling. But you may mind, that the walk muft rife a little in the midle, and yet the midle of the walke, and top of the Boxing of the Bordure muft be level, *i. e.* The Boxings fo much above the fide of the walk, as the midle of the walke is above its fides. Where your Boxing is timber or Stone, fill up the bordure of Earth to the top thereof, but where your Boxing is of box-juniper or the like, the Earth within the bordure and edg of the walks and pathes without, muft be equal.

As for the rife or fwell that walkes has which makes them Segmenta Circuli, grafs or brick walkes may have for 30 foot broad 6 Inches rife, for 20 foot 4 Inches, 10 foot 2 Inches; and let gravel have an Inch more proportionally: and it agrees with the rule of proport: in Arithmetick, as 20 is to 4: fo is 30 to 6. If gravell or brick walkes or pathes ly by the fide of grafs, make the grafs half Inche higher than fuch. If the walke be Grafs, make 2 foot Tables, or pathes of gravel betwixt it and the Bordure.

4. To

4. To lay grafs, firft level the ground, whither walke or plot; and its the better to ly a year fo made up, before you lay the turff; becaufe it may be levelled up again, if it fink unto holes: If it ly wet, bottome with Stones and Rubifh; and if the Earth be fat, take it out, and put in fand; however lay a foot thick fand immediatly under the Truff: then by the fquair ftreatch lines, Ritt with the Ritting Iron (which is an half round put into the end of a crooked ftick) & raife the Turff with the Turff-Spade, (which is broad mouthed, otherwife all one with the Husbandmens breaft-Turffing-fpade) let the Turff be of equal thicknefs, near Inch and half thick, a foot and half broad, and as much in length, lay their green fides together, when you put them in the cart, but do not Roll them when brought home, lay them all even and clofs; Feeling each particular Turff with your foot, fo as you may difcern any Inequallity, to be helped Immediatly, in laying ftill, beating every two three rowes of turff while moift, with the Timber beatters, and when the the whole is layed, and well beat, Roll well with the Stone-Roller, which fhould be as big as a hogfehead, The Spring and Autumne is the beft time. And if you mind to keep a good pile of Grafs, fuffer it never to grow Inch long: beat, mow, and Roll often, efpecially in the mornings and moift weather.

5. But if you would lay the hard tile or brick walkes, prepare as for Grafs, minding it wants the breadth of the brick of the true hight: for you muft fet them all on their edg clofs by other on a bed of lime, laying the fide, each other Row croffing the ends of the other, and place one in the midle of the walkes that both fides may be Regular.

6. To lay gravel, cleanfe firft the bottomes of the walkes of fat Earth, and Root weeds, and bottom it with Stones; and lay over that about half a foot of clean round gravel, and about three Inches top gravel of equal greatnefs which may be like beans and peafe: you muft make it thus equal by fifting, and fo Rake, Tred, and beat; and when compleatly levelled, beatt well with the Timber beaters, while moift, then Roll foundly with the Timber-Roller,

and

and afterwards with the Stone-Roller, especially in Rain, for which
the spring and Autumn is best; but if dry weather, you must dash
water one the Roller (continually in Rolling) with the watering pott,
and if you ar forced to use Sea or water sand, you may beat
some good clay to dust and mix with such, before you lay it; weed,
and Roll frequently.

7. For the orderly planting of flowers there may be three wayes,
as first in the Bordures of pleasure Gardens or Courts, plant 5
rowes in the bordure, and Intermixe them orderly *i. e.* divide and
plant every sundry sort through the whole Garden at equal distances, and not only so but every sundry colour thereof also; let never two of a kind nor two of a colour stand together, without o-
ther kinds and colours Interveening, so as there may not be two,
three of a kind or Colour at one end, Bordure, Plot or Place, and
non thereof through the rest, but universally and ornamentally Intermixt, and when you find a breach by some being past the flower,
you may have various Annual Flowers sowen in potts, ready to
plunge into the vacancies of the Bordures for continuing this beauty.

Secondly, in my sort of flower Gardens which is Bordures and
pathes running all one way *viz* : from the House, Plant 5 rowes
and intermix them, not as in the last way, but set 5 rowes of each
kind cross the Bordure, so as 25 of each sort may stand in a Geometrical squair.　As if you set a squair of Tulips, a squair of Boars-
ears a squair of Crocuses, a squair of July Flowers, a squair of
Anemonies, and a squair of Couslips : and so a squair of Tulips,
another of Boars Ears, &c : Through that Bordure Inter-
mixing the Colours of each sort, then may you make the next Bordure so Intermixt, but differing : minding that as you Intermix the
Bulbous and Fibrous in each Bordure, so must they be also in the
crossing, that the squair of Fibrous in this may oppose the squair of
Bulbous in the next, and likewayes whatever Bordure such sorts
ar in, on the one side of the walke, set the very same in the Bordure
equidistant from the walke on the other side, that the whole may

be

be Regular and uniformely Intermixt all the year, looking from all fides, ends or Angles.

Thridly in nurferies of Beds and Ridges, Plant every kind in thickets by themfelves, and Annualls and perennialls by themfelves (except only that you Intermix their Coloures) that is, make a whole Bed or Ridg of each kind, 6 Rowes in the Bed, the Dwarfifh may be 8 Rowes : thus every thicket of them Flowering in their own order, will have a great fhew, and at a great diftance; and here alfo obferve uniformity, that is, alike on each hand, fee the laft Chap: fect: 3. For if you have a Ridg or Bed of *July-flowers* or the like on the one fide, Plant another thereof at the fame place on the other, &c.

And becaufe Flowers muft be removed fome in one, two, or three years, and the Earth renued or enriched, and properly prepared, elfe they degenerate; (becaufe in long time they exhauft the fubftance of the ground, at leaft that part appropriate to them) therefore you have a good conveniency for effectuating the fame by thefe laft two models perfcribed : for often you will have fome Beds or fquairs where your Annualls ftood, to replant your Tulips, Anemonies or the like unto, and fo another fort where thefe ftood, and your Annualls again where this laft was; and becaufe here you remove a whole Bed or fquair of a kind at once, you may very conveniently prepare, Delve, Stir, Beat, fift and mix it throughly with the foyl proper (a thing moft neceffary) and this you could not well do, where they ar fcattred as in the firft way. See the Rules mentioned Part 2. Chap. 1. Sect. 10. and Chap. 7.

As to Terrafe walkes, if the Brow on which you make them, be not too fteep, the work fhall be the more Facile : if you build them up with walls, be careful to found deep enough according to the level, and if the midle of the terrafe be on the Central line of the houfe or of any walke, make the Stayr of the upmoft and downmoft there to part at a plat on the head going down at both fides, fo much of the ftayr cafe may be within as that the outter edg thereof may be in a line with the Bordure at the wall, by this it marrs not the

walke

walke, the reſt may be at the ends; Plant the Bordure at the upperſide of the walke with wall Trees, the under ſide (being but ell
high) with Laurels: &c. But if your Terraſe conſiſts only of walkes
and ſloping Banks, you may have the Bordure at the head and foot
of each Bank on either ſide the walkes, Planted with ſtandard cherries &c. and the Banks, of *Violets*, *Straw-Berries* or Graſs.

9. As for Pondes make them large and broad, ſuch being beſt
both for the health of Fiſh and Fowll, Clean, and moſt preferrable
water for watering Plants : ſquair, Triangle, Circle, Ovall, or
what figure fits your ground beſt ; let them be 5 or 6 foot of ſolid
water at leaſt, with Sluces to let it Run in and out at pleaſure.

I am againſt Arbuſt and cloſe walkes except Trees their natural
cloſing, where we have both ſhade and Air.

CHAP: 7.

How to Level Ground.

I Have often wiſhed that there might be ſome Rules found, whereby this expenſive worke might become more eaſy. There be two
ſorts of levelling *viz* : the Horizontal, and Sloping. The firſt
is beſt known, but the laſt more profitable and convenient. Example, 1 have made a plot ſlop 4 foot in 200 long, and 18 Inches
in 380 foot the other way: this was not perſpicuous to vulgar eyes,
yet to have made it Horizontal, would have been Ridiculous as
to time, paines and expences. And in levelling the walkes about a
plot (which ſloped naturally) to make them correſpond with the
grow_nd rownd, I behoved to make the midle walk agree with the
ſide ones whereupon it ſlops 10 foot in 370 long: now if I had made
this Horizontal, it would have been 5 foot or 10 ſteps lower than
the one ſide walke, and as much higher than the other, and ſo
worſe and more Inconvenient than before, both as it is a walke,

and

and anent Correſpondancy with the reſt of the ground within;there-
fore I am for levelling any ground ſloping, that it may turn a little
to the Sun if poſſible, for drawing water, that it may correſpond
with its adjunčts, and above all to prevent the more coſtly way:
for Its certainly a principal obſervation in levelling, not only to
cauſe, the ground of it ſelf ſerve it ſelf, but alſo to level it as it lyes
moſt conveniently, which is the cheap and eaſie way of levelling.
When you have a Row of ſtakes ſet in a ſtraight line and about 20
foot diſtance, as in the edge of a Bordure or midle of a walke, the
way of levelling them either Horizontal or ſloping, is to mark
and put a nail in the two Stakes which ar at the extreams or ends
thereof, and view betwixt, cauſe marke all the Reſt which ar betwixt, in a level line, therewith; This is the eaſieſt, the exačteſt
and quickeſt way: and in the ſame methode you may go round any
plot, and conſequently croſs (every way) the ſame accordingly.

In that which you would have Horizontal, place the long Rule
and the level at one end, ſuppoſe the ſole of the Door, till the
plumb fall right in recovering, and view alongſt the ſaid Rule (as
on a fowlling piece) that you may ſee what part of each Stake it hits,
and cauſe one with a piece white paper or white hefted knife hold
the ſame at each ſtake, its heft tending out (as the nails which carry
up the line)and direčt him by words or ſignes to hold up or down till
it be Juſt level : when they ar all marked, meaſure down ſo much
on each Stake, as was raiſed up for conveniency; in viewing there
marke, put in nailes a little, ſtreatch on the line, and level up the
earth or gravel thereunto.

And where you would have determin'd ſlops,ſet on the level and
marke the far-end ſtake in a level line therewith, then meaſure down
upon the ſaid Stake or pole from the marked place ſo much as you
deſigne the ſlop, and put in a naile with white paper about it, and
at the upperſide of the Rule in the ſtake at the door, put in another
nail, and by viewing betwixt theſe two, marke all the reſt as before.
If the diſtance betwixt the extreams be farr where the ſight may
dazle, let the viewer deſcent his ſtation, and come foreward at
every

every 5 or 6 Stakes and holding his knife at the laſt marked Stake, cauſe his aſſiſtant or ſtake-marker proceed.

To level as the ground lyes, let its ſlop be what it will you need neither level nor Rule (except you pleaſe to try how much it ſlops after its done for ſatisfaction) only ſet ſtakes as before, and viewing the ground narrowly put nails in the ſtakes which are at the extreams where you think the ground will Run when levelled to make it ſerve it ſelf, and as it lyes beſt or eaſieſt for levelling : and when you have concluded upon the level at the extreams, make all the ſtakes in the Intervall by viewing as above.

2. But to proportion the level to the ground is the whole art of levelling. Its true it is eaſie, if you have a plot or walke a foot higher at one end, to take half a foot thereof, and lay on the low end ſo as the two ends may be Horizontal, (I have already ſhew'd how to level having the two ends found) or if it be Horizontal to take 9 Inches off the one end, and lay on the other, that it may ſlop 18 Inches : but if ſome places of it ly one way, and ſome another, and ſome neither the one nor the other, this increaſeth the difficulty. Wherefore you muſt firſt drive ſtakes at the corners of the plot, then view the ground about and put nayles in the ſtakes where you would have the level Run, or at leaſt where you think by your eye it may moſt conveniently come to make it contain it ſelf, and eaſieſt to be levelled : alſo ſet up ſeveral ſtakes in the Intervalls and Croſswayes through the plot from oppoſite Angles, and by viewing betwixt the foreſaid nailes every way marke all the ſtakes level ; but if you cannot ſee from the markes of this ſuppoſed level which are on theſe corner ſtakes, ſeeing there may be ſome underneath the ground, little Hills, or ſome ſuch obſtructions in the way, then meaſure equally up upon each of them, ſo farr as you think convenient for getting your ſight, and mind to take down the ſame again after viewing.

When all is marked with this ſuppoſed level, go over and note narrowly how it will agree, that ſo as your reaſon ſhall teach you to alter, take up one end or down the other, or up or down both till

                         you

you bring it to such proportion, as to do its own busines it self. Or you may do more exactly thus.

Suppose you have a Bordure or midle of a walke with sixteen stakes driven therein at 20 foot distance, all marked with a supposed level, and 10 of their markes above ground, and 6 under ground : first measure how farr the markes on each of the 10 stakes is above ground, and write them down particulai ly, and adding their measures together, you find 13 foot 4 Inches. Secondly measure how farr the markes of the 6 stakes ar under ground, & write down, adding them together you find it 12 foot ; substract the one from the other and the difference is 16 Inches which must be divided by 16 the stakes in the Bordure, that is, aneInch to each stake, so that this supposed level is an Inch higher over all than the true level, which being taken down will make the ground there level it self, and no more. This may suffice for example, but I could say more, if I did see your ground. And if you can thus proportion the level to one Bordure, walke, or one Row of stakes, you may by the same Rule find the level for the stakes round aud cross the plot, and consequently level the same accordingly : for having once concluded on the level, drive stakes over all the plot as in my first way of planting Trees, (see Chap. 4. Sect 4.) and marke and put nailes therein as above is taught for carrying the line. Except you mean to follow my method of levelling the Kitchen-Garden, or the like for planting and sowing, which is only to level one Bordure thus by stakes and lines. Round each plot and by the eye level up the ground within thereunto all along in Trenching, albeit this not so proper for Courts and Grass plots. However as by this means, I use to level ground without a level, so do I think this way of finding out the true level by means of a supposed one, worthy your notice, and if rightly improven save you much money and paines.

Be cautious in founding your Walls lest you undermine them in levelling, nor is it convenient sometimes to confine your level to the foundation of Walls already built : for in so doing, you may lose more, than would cast down and rebuild, but in such cases you may rather build under gradually.　　　　　　　　3. There

3. There be some bad lying plots and walkes, with an ascent at the head, hollow in the midle, level at the foot, these and the like are very troublesome to level under one denomination: for the taking down the Hill, bares it so, that plants cannot prosper thereon. some ar necessitate to take out the Gravel, Tile, or Stones so much deeper, and travell earth again : but I rather advise to make terrases, you need not confine to the number of banks, but only to the proportion and uniformity. If it tend all one way as high at one end and low at the other, then its proper enough for perpendicular walkes that front the house, but if low in the midle and high at both ends, or low at both ends and high in the midle, then more proper for Parallel walkes, (whose extremities are equidistant from the central line of the House) remember to divide and slop them equally.

This minds me of some abuses, which I have seen, as a plot of sloping levelled ground, with another Horizontaly levelled lying at the foot thereof, (at least not under one slop) or Horizontal walkes and bordures lying by the foot and head of sloping plots ; these are unseemly : for you should allwayes make them slop under the same denomination (except in steep and high banks) I have made walkes of 18 foot broad slop 18 Inches from one side to the other, because the whole plot sloped the same way, so much proportionally, yet to the eye appears very pleasant ; but where such Horizontal and sloping pieces ly contiguous, the defect is easily seen, therefore if you be necessitate to lay some plots so, (albeit I know reason for laying walkes so) make rather a Hedg to Intercept, and in all your workes let there be a connexion.

4. There be some more obstructions in levelling, as in a long walke when you have the two ends found and marked, (either with a supposed or true level) and cannot see betwixt, to do it exactly by reason of length : here two may go to the midle or near it, where you may conveniently see both ends, looking back and fore, there drive in two stakes near the length of the long straight Rules distance, at which hold on the Rule, and let one view alongst the same till the marke at the West-end be level therewith, and the

other

other towards the East till the marke there be also level with the same; so both may alter up or down till they have their defires at once : then fix the Rule, and having as many stakes set as is need-full, you may view backsight and foresight hereon, and level them all exactly.

5. But if a Wall, a House, &c. Intercept, measure perpendi-cular and exactly up to the top thereof, and on the other side mea-sure down the same again; and so set foreward the level, but so as it may communicate with the rest, when obstructions are removed.

But if a Hill, go to the Top, set the Rule level, and laying ane eye thereto, cause one with a long pole go down till its Top be le-vel therewith (he holding it level by a Plumb Rule) then defcent your stations and set the upper-end of the Rule where the pole stood, there level it and do as before :. thus from station to station to the foot of the Hill, (if it be so great) keeping compt in a Note-book what poles and parts; the which may be as easily taken down the other side by the same method.

But if it be possible to see over the obstruction on 3 footed stand-ing leathers by help of long poles or Pikes, (as I have done in the like case) raife your level thereon, and having viewed, and mar-ked that on the other side, measure down the same there, &c.

6. I might here speak of the solidity of earth, whereby you may move readily compt the expence of levelling, but having shew'd in the next Chap. Sect. 5. How to measure solids, I presume its appli-cable to earth : (as well as Timber, Stone, &c.) For if you know the breadth, length, and deepth thereof, you may find how ma-ny solid Ells, &c. And if you know how many Ells and parts will load a cart and how many carts a day, you may go near to calculat the cost of the whole.

7. In levelling any ground for Kitchen ground, Orchards, or Nurseries, take not away its good earth or surface, (as you bring down the hights) but alwayes turn over the upper-part thereof be-hind you, carrying away that which is below, so much deeper, that it may contain that surface, and put the bad earth in bottom of hollowes with better mould above it.

In

In the practife of levelling (or other workes) contrive the work-ing, fo as there may be ftill a motion amongft all the partes; and albeit carts are cheaper for levelling than Wheell-barrowes, if the way of carriage be not very fhort., yet if you do not fet as many men to fill the carts as may have the one full againft the other come in and no more, you lofe confiderably : and this will be according to the diftance of carriage, or as the earth is capable of being wrought; and fo with Wheell-barrowes for two Wheellers, three barrowes, and one filler fometimes doth well, fometimes more fil-lers or fewer Wheellers, yet ftill let them have a led barrow. And if this could be done with carts alfo, it would be of great Advantage. wherefore in my opinion there is no way fo probable to worke this effect, as the carts with three Wheells where by 2. men, with 2. of them carts, and one Horfe can do as much as three Men, two Horfes, and 2 Carts: for one man to fill the led Cart, the other Man to drive the one Horfe : and when he comes in, he has nothing to do but take the Trafes and Hooks off the empty Cart and put upon the rings of the full one and fo drive on. This Cart has no Trams or Limbers, but a Swingle-Tree or Breaft-board be-fore, where the rings that keeps the Traffes are : it has a handfome folding body, the thrid Wheell is about 3 o Inches Diameter all Iron and Runs in a Shiers of the fame faftned perpendicular under the midle of the forebreaft with a turning Pin of Iron; the other two Wheells are common, but if they have an Iron Axis, the better.

8. To bring in Water in Pipes to your Houfes, Courts, Gar-dens, Pondes, Parks, &c. Confider on the level, for as the place where you convey it unto, muft allwayes be lower than the Fountain from whence it comes, elfe thither it cannot flow : fo muft you take notice that no Hill in the way of its conveyance be fo high as the Fountain it felf. You may find the level by placing your In-ftrument at the Well or Fountain, as I directed in walkes. and if a Hill intercept that fight, plant on the Top thereof, that by back-fight and forefight you may find the difference, that hence you may know whither you can carry it about the obftruction : but if

the

the diſtance be farr, you need to be the more exact. As for Inſtru-
ment, the Croſs diſcribed Chap. 3. whoſe ſights may be two Pro-
ſpect Glaſſes, may do well whither for one or many ſtations. Let
one ſtand at the Spring-head, another betwixt and the place whereunto you deſire to carry the Water, a large diſtance ſundry, but ſo
as a thrid man about the midle may ſee both their Marke-boards
that is on their Pikſtaves, and direct them to hold level by his back
and foreſight, deſiring them to keep accompt what foot and parts:
and ſo come foreward till the aſſiſtant at the well plant where the
foremoſt ſtood, and thus proceed all in a ſtraight line, and do as
before, from ſtation to ſtation ſo long as needfull. at length add
all the meaſures of back-ſtations together, and all of the fore-ſta-
tions : ſubſtract the one from the other, and the remainders gives
the difference of levels betwixt the Fountain and the appointed
place.

　　Allow to the fall of the Water for every 1000 foot in length 12
Inches ſlop at leaſt.

CHAP. VIII.

How to meaſure, divide and lay out Land, &c.

SOme following other-Countrey-books Ignorantly meaſures our
ground with their meaſures, therefore I am here to Informe
ſuch that,

　　In meaſuring all figures whither ſuperficial or ſolide, it is requi-
ſit to know firſt, wherewith they ſhould be meaſured, ſecondly how
they ſhould be meaſured.

　　Land is done by ell, or fall meaſure, (alſo Maſons Roughwork-
buildings) Stone, Board, and Glaſs by foot meaſure : 12 Inches
a foot (and no diſtinction betwixt a Scots and Engliſh foot) the Gla-
ziers

ziers ufed only 8 Inches, but the Act of Parliament hath reduced them
to 12 as others. Some would think 12 Inches but a thrid part more,
whereas it is equivalent to $2\frac{1}{4}$ of theirs : for 8 times 8 is 64, and
12 times 12 is 144, out of which I get 2 times 64, and the 16 remaining is $\frac{1}{4}$ thereof. This minds me of that queftion *viz.* Whither
is a fquair half foot or half a foot fquair moft ? I have heard feveralls
fay they were both alike, but this was their miftake : For a half
foot fquair (fuperficial,) is but the half of a fquair half foot, and if
folid its but $\frac{1}{8}$ thereof.

The Scots Ell according to feveral Acts of Parliament is three
foot one Inch, or 37 Inches long : 6 ells long and 6 ells broad is 36,
a fall fquair : 10 falls in length and 4 in breadth is 40, a Rood fquair :
40 falls in length and 4 in breadth is 160, an Acre. See the Table
of fuperficial fquair meafure. And thefe that defires long meafure,
6 ells long is a fall, 40 falls a furlong, 8 furlongs a mile. See the
Table.

A Table of Superficial fquair meafure, according to Scotland.

Acres	4	160	5760
	Roods	40	1440
		Falls	36
			Ells

A Table of Superficial long meafure, according to Scotland.

Ells			
6	Falls		
240	40	furlongs	
1920	320	8	Mile

We

We differ in measuring land from the English, as the fall differs from the pole : our fall is 6 clls or 18½ foot, their pole is 5½ yardes or 16½ foot.

By what is said I hope you know wherewith to measure, it only remaines then that you know how to measure; of which anon.

2. In measuring all superficies we take notice of the breadth and length, but of solides the breadth, length and deepth. To instance in a few, and first of some Superficial Figures; as a Geometrical squair, (see fig 18.) it is measured by multiplying one side in it self *(viz. a. b.* or *c·e :* or *a. c.* or *b. c.)* which here is 30½ falls : In your workings I would advise you to make use of decimal Arithmetick, because thereby you may work whole Numbers and Fractions together with great ease and quicknels, and you may reduce ordinary Fractions into decimalls, by multiplying the Numerator by 100. or 1000. &c. and dividing the product by the Denominator, so shall the ¼ of any thing be 25, the ½ 5, and the ¾ 75 : therefore

multiply 30. 5 in its self, the product is 930. 25. which is 930. falls and ¼ of a fall. See the example, for when you multiply decimally what ever fractions are in multiplicand and multiplicator, cut them off after addition: the which if there be any will be Fractions, as here you see

30. 5
30. 5
1525
9150
930·25

two cut off *viz.* 25 which is ¼ of 100, the fall being here into 100 parts the Integer of 25. And when you divide decimally, as whole Numbers and Fractions by whole Numbers, put still a dash betwixt the whole and Fraction, and notice how often you will get your divisor placed under the whole Numbers of your dividend, and just so many whole Numbers will be in the quotient and the rest Fractions: or if you divide whole and Fractions by whole and Fractions, notice how many times you may place the whole Numbers of divisor under whole Numbers of dividend &c. Or if you divide whole Numbers by whole and Fractions, whatever Fractions be in divisor add so many Ciphers to the dividend, and do as before.

You may reduce this (or any other) plot into Acres by dividing
by

by 160 the falls in one Acre, and the product here will be 5 Acres
130 falls and ¼ of a fall.   But if
you would further know what this
Fraction (25) is in Ells, say, if 100
be equall to 36 the ells in one fall
what is 25 equall unto? Multiply
the 2d Number by the 3d, and di-
vide by the firſt and the anſwer will be 9 ells.   See it wrought.

		36	1
		25	43
900 (9		180	930 (5
100		72	160
		900	

Moreover falls may be reduced into poles, and poles into falls,
or *Scots* meaſure into *Engliſh* or *Engliſh* into *Scots* : one ſuperficies
is to another as the ſquairs of their like ſides, therefore as the ſquair
of 16.5 (the *Engliſh*)is to the ſquair of 18.5 (the *Scots*) ſo is the content in *Scots* Acres or falls,to the content in *Engliſh* Acres or poles.

Example the ſquair of 16.5 *(i.e.* 16.5 multiplyed in it ſelf *)* is
272.25 and the ſquair of 18.5 is 342.25, And as 272.25 is to
342.25 : ſo is 930.25 (the content of the ſaid plot in falls or *Scots*
meaſure) to 1169.43¾ ſere, its content in poles. or *Engliſh* meaſure.
This I thought fit to mention, to let any ſee that knows not the difference betwixt the *Engliſh* meaſure and ours.

Secondly an oblong ſquair or Parallelogram (ſee fig. 19.) by multiplying the breadth by the length : *a. d.* or *b. c.* is its length and *a. b.*
or *d. c.* its breadth.

Thridly, a Triangle, (ſee fig. 20.) all Triangles are meaſured by
multiplying the whole baſe by half the perpendicular or whole
perpend: by half the baſe; *a. b.* is baſe and *i. c.* the perpendicular, or
without the perpendicular at all, add up all the ſides, and take half
the ſumme; from this halfſumme take every ſide, which call the
three differences, multiply theſe three differences and the half
ſumme continually together, the ſquair Root of the laſt product
ſhall be the Area of the Triangle.

Fourthly, a Trapezia *(*ſee fig. 21.*)* is reduced into two Triangles, and meaſured accordingly.

Fifthly, and ſo is any irregular ſtraight lined figure, and if any
ſide of it be crooked, draw a line that may leave out as much as it
takes in. But if it cannot be meaſured within becauſe of obſtructions,

then add on the outfide till you reduce it into a fquair, and after multiplication fubftract what was added, the remainder fhall be its Area.

Sixthly a circle (See Fig: 22.) is near equall to a fquair made of $\frac{1}{2}$ the diameter and $\frac{1}{2}$ the circumference or perifery, and therefore is meafured by multiplying $a.q.c.o.b.$ the Semicircumference by $a. d.$ or $d.c.$ the femidiameter. And having any one given you may find the other by the Rule of proportion thus:

The loweft number is, as 7. is to 22: fo is the diameter to the Circumference, or as 22. is to 7: fo the Circumference to the diameter, or thus: As 1. is to 3.1416: fo the Diameter to the Circum: or as 3.1416. is to 1: fo the Circum: to the diam: or as 113. to 355: fo diam: to perifery, or as 355. to 113: fo perifery to diameter.

In this the Diameter is 63 falls and as 7. is to 22: fo 63 (the diam:) to 198 (the perifery) Take $\frac{1}{2}$ perifery which is 99. and multiply by $\frac{1}{2}$: Diameter which is 31.5. and the product is 3118.5. or as 28. is to 22: or 14. to 11: or 1. to 785399: fo is the fquair of the Diameter to the Area of the circle: or as 22. to 28: or 11. to 14: or 355. to 452: or 1. to 1.273239: fo is the Area of the Circle to the fquair of its diameter. as 1. is to 282095: fo is the circle to the Root of a fquair equall to the Area of the circle. as 1. is to 707107: fo is the Diameter to the Root of a fquair to be infcribed in a Circle. as 1. is to 225072: fo is the perifery to the Root of the infcribed fquair in the circle, and as 1. is to 886227: fo is the Diameter to the Root of a fquair equall to the Circle, which is the fquairing of a Circle.

Seventhly., the Semicircle is meafured by multiplying the Radius or femidiameter by $\frac{1}{4}$ of the circumference of the whole Circle.

Eightly, the Quadrant or $\frac{1}{4}$ of the Circle, by multiplying the Radius by $\frac{1}{2}$ of that Arch line which is $\frac{1}{8}$ of the perifery.

Ninthly, to meafure the fegment of a Circle as $q.i.o.c.$ firft draw its Radius from $d.$ to $o.$ which conftituts the Sector $d.o.c.$ And as the Quadrant hath 90 degrees fo this Sector hath 40: therefore fay,

as

as 90.is to the content of the Quadrant:so is 40.to the content of the sector, the Triangle *d. o. i.* Being substracted from the Sectors content, Rests half the segment, that doubled is the Area of the whole.

To do Geometrically, find the length of its Arch line thus :(See Fg.23.) divide the chord line *a. d. c.* Of that arch into 4 equall parts set one of these from *c.* to *i.* on the chord line, and one of them from the Angle at *a.* to. *o.* In the Arch line , then draw the line *o. i.* which line is half the length of the Arch line , *a. o. b. c.* (but if the part of a Circle be greater than a semicircle,then divide the Arch line into two equall parts and find the length of one of these as is taught, which doubled is the half length of the whole.) here take the half of the Arch line of Fig: 23. And multiply by its Radius *e. b.* The product is the Area of the segment *a. b. c. d.* and the Triangle *a. c. e.* which Triangle must be substracted therefrom, and the remainder is the Area of the segment.

Tenthly, if you would measure the oval, then observe the Rules in measuring the segment: seing the oval is made of segments; If it be from two Centers, then its but two Segments, If from four, then it is four segments and a quadrangle.

Eleventhly Regular poligons ar such figures as consist of equall sides and Angles,and which may be inscribed in a Circle or Circumscribed about a Circle, whither pentagon 5 sided, hexagon six sided, Heptagon , Octagon , Nonagon , Decagon, Dodecagon, for any of these take half the compass about and the perpend : drawen from the Centre to the midle of one of the sides, multiply the one by the other,and that gives the content.

Twelvthly to measure any Irregular figure consisting of straight and Circular lines, the arches and angles bending Inwards ; If you cannot reduce them into some of the Figures above mentioned within it self, you may do it by drawing lines without : and after you have multiplied, substract what was added (whither segments or others) and there will remain the Area of the figure proposed.

Mountains and Valleyes ar best reduced into Triangles , and so
mea-

meafured: for albeit they make rather fpherical than plain Triangles, yet the way of menfuration differs not ; yet as in plain Trapezias there are other wayes than by Triangles (as taking the half of both ends and fides added for the mean breadth and length) fo for mounts and Valleyes, *viz* : Meafure the circuite or bafe part of the Mountain and its top, add them together, and take half of that fum for the length; do fo with the afcenfe (or going up from foot to top) of 2 fides of the Hill, add the meafure of the longeft and fhorteft fide together, taking the half thereof for the breadth, and multiply the one by the other, that gives the fuperficies of the Mount or Hill.

And as you meafured the compafs of the foot of the Hill fo muft you round the circuite or compafs of the hight of the valley or glen: and as you meafured the top of the Mountain, fo muft you the bottom of the depth of the valey ; add them together and take half thereof for the breadth. likwayes as you meafured the afcenfe of both fides of the Hill, fo muft you the defcenfe or going down of both fides to the bottom of the valley ; add them together, and take half for the length, and fo multiply as before.

3. Albeit I have faid enough anent meafuring land, yet there is much more required in dividing and laying out the fame.

The firft time I faw the need of it, was in making an Avenue of great length which croffed a march feveral times, which did take in feveral pieces of land and caft out others, but non of them being equal neither in fhape nor proportion, I behoved to meafure both, and then cut off fo much as might Ballance, and that from parts affigned.

As firft, if from the Triangle *a. b. c.* (being Fig: 24.) which containes 870 falls fquair, you would cut off 300 falls fquair, then finding the bafe *c. b.* of this Triangle to be 58 falls long, fay, if 870 falls (the whole plot) have 58 for its bafe : what will 300 (the part I defire off) have for its bafe.

Anfwer

Anſwer, 20. therefore meaſure
alongſt 20 falls on the baſe from　　I
one end thereof, as from *b.* to *d.*　　17400 (20
then draw the line *a. d.* ſo ſhall　　8770
a. b. d. contain 300 falls, and *a.*　　8
d. c. 570. Or

```
    300
     58
   2400
   1500
  17400
```

If it be required to take off part from a Triangle, according to
any proportion given, by a line drawn parallel to any of the ſides
aſſigned, as let *a b. c.* (which is Fig. 25.) be a Triangle containing
7 Acres, or 1120 falls; and it is deſired that 2 Acres be cut off by
a line drawn Parallel to *a. c.* Its baſe line is 57 falls which you muſt
divide in proportion, as 5. is to 2. in the point *d.* then ſeek the mean
proportional between *b. d.* 42. and *b. c.* 57. as *b. f.* 48 $\frac{8}{27}$ But having
(as in the end of this Chap:) ſhewed how to find mean proportionals
Arithmetically, I ſhall here ſhew you how to do Geometrically.

Therefore deſcribe the ſemicircle *b. e. c.* and at the point *d.* on the
baſe line, raiſe the Perpendicular *d e.* Cutting the Arch line in *e.*
then ſet the length of *b. e.* (which is the mean Proportional) from *b.*
on the Diameter line, and that will reach to the point *f.* now from
the point at *f.* take the neareſt diſtance to the line *c. a.* and ſet that
diſtance ſquair off at *a.* to *G.* then draw the line *G. f.* exactly parallel to *a. c.* ſo will the Triangle *G. b. f.* be 5 Acres, and *G. f. c. a.* 2
Acres, the thing propounded.

If you would cut off ſome part from a ſquair parallel to one ſide,
you need only meaſure that ſide, whence you deſigne to take it at;
and divide the parts, you ar to take off thereby: and the quotient
ſhall tell how much you muſt ſet off. Example by fig: 19. its ane
oblong ſquair denominated *a. b. c. d.* I deſire 3 Acres or 480 falls,
cut off at, and parallel to the ſide *a. b.* which ſide is 32 falls divide
480 (the part you ar to cut off) by 32 (the ſide of the ſquair) and
the quotient will be 15 therefore ſet off 15 falls from *a.* to *e.* and
from *b.* to *f.* and the ſquair *a. b. f. e.* is 3 Acres, as was required.

But if its ſides did not go ſquair off, as the Trapezia 21 then reduce the Trapezia into a Triangle. and divide the baſe into ſo many
H

equal

equal or unequal parts, (as you would have the Trapezia into) then find a mean proportion between the extream points of the bafe, and every particular point in the bafe: from which means draw lines through the Trapezia parallel to the fide affigned, which may an-fwere your requiring. Or

A more ready way to work on ground, is to find the mid line of the ground you are to cut off, and divide thereby, &c. But the queftion, is how to effect this, you may firft fet off the whole in two Triangles, *viz:* If you would cut off 160 falls, at the end *a. b.* of fig: 21. Then fet off the half thereof at the Angle *c. a. b.* to cut the line *a. c.* by the firft: for you will find that as the Triangle *c. a. b.* containes 364 falls, fo muft you go 7 ⅔ from *a.* to *e.* on that bafe, to draw the line *b. e.* that Cuts off the Triangle *a. b. e.* containing 80 falls. Likwayes as the Triangle *d. e. b.* containes 165 ½, fo muft you go from *b.* to *f.* that, *a. b. e. f.* may containe 160 falls. Only the line *e. f.* is not parallel to *a. b.* therefore as *b. f.* is 5 longer than *a. e.* fet 2 ½ out from *e.* to G. and in from *f.* to *h.* and draw the line G. *h.* paral-lel to *a. b.* and to leave as much out as it takes in; then find the length of the mid line betwixt *a. b* and G. *h. viz. i.* κ. which is 16. and by the fame divide 160. the quotient fhall be 10. And that will reach from *a.* to G. and from *b.* to *h.* fo as to cut off 160 falls at, and parallel to the end *a. b.* (by the line G. *h.*) as was defired.

It is required to part the pentagon or fig: 26. Into two equal parts from the Angle at *a.* The whole figure is 10 Acers, one Rood and 12 falls, that is, 1652 falls; then the half is 826. and the Tri-angle *a. b. c.* is but 441. which wants 385 of the half: therefore take 385 from the Triangle *a. c. d.* by the firft Rule, and there will be ad-ded the Triangle *a. c. f.* to the Triangle *a. b. c.* which will divide the figure into two equal parts, the thing required.

I am defired to fet off a thrid part of the hexagon or fig: 27. By a line drawen from the point G. the whole plot is 45 Acers and 145 falls or 7345 falls, the ⅓ thereof is 2448. and the Trapezia G. *e. f. a.* is but 2041. 875. which wants 407 falls: (and the fraction which is a little more than ⅚ of a fall) wherefore I muft take 407. 875 from the

Trian_

t

he Triangle *G.d.e.* by the firſt, thus. If 2523. 50 the content of the Triangle *G.d.e.* have for its baſe *c.d.* 62 falls, how farr muſt I go on the ſame to get off 407.875 ? anſwer, 10 $\frac{5325}{15235}$ that is 10 falls and about $\frac{1}{5}$ of a fall; the which being ſet from *e.* to *h.* to draw the line *G.h* parts off the $\frac{1}{3}$ of this Irregular hexagon, as was deſired.

If you were deſired to lay out any number of Acres at pleaſure into a Geometrical ſquair, you need only reduce them into falls and extract the ſquair Root thereof (as at the end of this Chap.) which is the length of one ſide, and ſo meaſure, or ſet off by a Chain. Or

If you would have it ly in a Parallelogram or oblong ſquair, you may lay it out, as I directed for cutting off ſome part from a ſquair parallel to one ſide : for knowing how many falls you would have into the oblong ſquair, you may make a ſide at pleaſure (if not already confin'd to one) and divide thereby as is taught. Or

If you would make a Triangle to contain ſo many Acres, Roods, or falls, double the number of falls, then take for the baſe of your Triangle, any number at pleaſure, by which divide the double of falls to be brought in the Triangle; and the quotient ſhall be the perpendicular to that Triangle, whoſe content ſhall be the number of falls propoſed. And herein conſiſts the Reduction of figures Arithmetical.

4. Perhaps you may have occaſion, to meaſure the ſolidity of Earth, Timber Trees, Stones, &c. Now to find the ſuperficies of ſolides. as,

Firſt the Sphære or Globe. multiply its whole circumference by its whole diameter, and that gives its ſuperficial content. And as 7 is to 22 : or 113. to 355 : ſo is the Diameters ſquair to the ſuperficies of the ſphære : and ſo is the Diameter multiplyed by the axis of a cylinder to its ſuperficies: and ſo is half Diameter of a cone multiplyed in its ſide to the ſuperficies of a cone: and ſo the ſquair of the chord of half the ſegment of a ſphere to the ſuperficies of that ſegment.

As 1. is to 1.772454 : ſo is the Diameter to the Root of a ſquair equal to the ſuperficies of a Sphære. Or as 1. is to; 564189 : ſo is

the Circumference to the Rootſquair, that ſhall be equal to the ſuperficies of the Sphere.

5. As ſuperficial meaſure hath 144 Inches ſquair in one foot : ſo
ſolide meaſure hath 1728. every ſolide foot is like a Die, for what
it wants either in breadth or thickneſs it muſt have in length : for 12
times 12. is 144, and 12 times 144. is 1728. the cubeſquair Inches
in a cubeſquair foot; therefore,

In meaſuring a ſquair ſolide, multiply its length by its breadth,
and that product by its deepth.

To meaſure a Cylinder (ſuch as a Roller) multiply the Semi-
diameter by the Semi-circumference, and that product by the
length.

To meaſure a Cone (viz. it hath a Circular baſe, and ends in a
ſharp point) take the ſuperficial content of the baſe, and multiply by
⅓ of the altitude or hight.

To meaſure a Pyramid (viz. it hath an angular baſe, and ends in
a ſharp point) make uſe of the laſt Rule.

To meaſure a Sphere or Globe, (viz. a ſolid figure every where
equidiſtant from the Centre) Cub the Diameter, and multiply
that by 11. then divide that product by 21. the quotient is the ſolide
content of the Sphere.

As 1. is to 80604 : ſo is the Diameter to the Root of a Cube
equal to the Sphere. Or as 1. is to ;256556 : ſo is the Circumference to the Root Cube of a ſolide, equal to the Sphere.

As 1. is to 523599 : ſo the Cube of the Diameter to the Sphere.
Or as 1. is to ;909856 : ſo is the Sphere to the Cube of the Diameter.

As 1. is to ;016887 : ſo is the Cube of the Circumference to the
Sphere. or as 1. is to 59;217629 : ſo is the Sphere to the Cube of
the Circumference.

As 42. is to 22 : or 1. to 5236 : ſo is the Diameter cubed to the
ſolidity of the Sphere. Or as 22. is to 42 : or 1. to 1;90986 : ſo
is the ſolidity of the Sphere to its Diameter cubed.

As 28. is to 22 : or 14. to 11 : or 1. to 785399 : ſo is the ſquair
of

of the Diameter of a Cylinder multiplyed by its *side*, to the folidity of the Cylinder : and fo is the fquair of the Diameter of a Cone multiplyed by ⅓ of its Axis, to the folidity of the Cone.

As 1 . is to 2 5 ; 1 3 2 7 : fo is the Diameter cubed to a Cylinder.

To meafure a Regular Polygon, (as a piece Timber hewed into 5 , 6 , 7 , 8 , &c. Equal fides with both ends alike) multiply the femicircumference by the Radius or femi-diameter, and that product by the length.

To meafure a Truncus, (*viz.* a Cylinder that leans) take the fuperficies of the Circle, and adding the longer and fhorter fides of the Truncus, take the half for the hight.

The Sector of a Sphere is meafured by multiplying its fuperficies Spherical by one third of the hight.

The Segment of a Sphere meafure it as a Sector, and fubftract from the Sector the folidity of a Cone, whofe Apex is in the Center, and bafe the Area of the Segment.

The folidity of a Spheroid is got by multiplying the greateft Circle into two thirds of the Axis about which the Spheroid is made.

The folidity of the Trunk of a Spheroid cut off with two Circles at right angles with the bafe, fuch as our Wine Cafkes are, is gotten by adding two thirds of the Area of the Circle at the bung or midle together, and multiplying the fame by the length.

Irregular diforderly Solids ar meafured by help of Water in a prepared Veffel exactly cubical, fo large as it may contain it ; according to *Archimedes* : put the body into the veffel, pour in fo much Water as may juft cover the fame ; and make a marke where the fuperficies of the Water touched the veffel ; take out the fame irregular body, and make a fecond marke where the fuperficies cuts the fide of the veffel ; then take the diftance between the two markes in Inches and parts, which multiply by the fquair of the fide of the prepared veffel ; and that product fhall be the folidity of the irregular body fought.

6, If you would meafure any fuperficies by the Table of Logarithms, then fet down the Logar : of the length and breadth, add them together, and whatever their fumme be, the number anfwering thereunto is the Area or fuperficial content. Which if they be falls and you defire to reduce them into Acres, then out of the Logarithm thereof fubftract the Logarithm of 160 (the falls in one Acre) and there fhall remain the Logarithm of the content in Acres. Or

If you would meafure folides by the Table, fet down the Logarithms of its length, breadth, and deepth : add them together; and the abfolute Number anfwering this Logarithm is the folide content required.

Alfo by the Table you may extract the fquair Root (of any plot, field or other fuperficies) with great eafe and quicknefs thus :

Take the half of the Logarithm of the given Number whofe Root is required, and the Number anfwering this Logarithm is the fquair Root fought. Or

For extraction of the Cube Root of any folide, take the third part of the Logarithm of the given Number whofe Root is required, and the abfolute Number anfwering thereunto is the Cube Root defired.

And to find a mean proportional (between two Numbers given by the Table) is to add the Logarithms of them together, and take half. As if you would have the mean betwixt 40. 5. and 72. Thus :

The Logarithm of 40. 5 is	.	.		1.607422
The Logarithm of 72 is		.	.	1.857290
The fummes added	.	.	.	3.464712
The half of the Logarithm is	.	.	.	1.732356

The Number anfwering this Logarithm is 54. for the mean proportional.

To find 2, 3, 4, 5, &c. means between any two Numbers, take their difference, and divide it by a Number more by one than the Number of means defired, as if 3 means, divide by 4. &c. This Logarithmical quotient added to the laft, finds the firft mean next it, it, &c.　As, if you would have three mean proportionalls betwixt 4. and 64.

The Logarithm of 64. is　　　　⁚　　:	1.806180
The Logarithm of 4. is　　　．　　．　．	0.602060
The difference is　　．　　．　　．　．	1.204120

The $\frac{1}{4}$ thereof is 0.301030. which being added to the Logarithm of 4 makes 0.903090. the Logarithm of 8. for the first mean : again added to this last, gives 1.204120. the Logarithm of 16. and added to this, gives 1.505150. the Logarithm of 32. which 8.16.32. ar the 3 means betwixt 4. and 64.

But because the extraction of the squair Root is so needful to be known, I shall demonstrate the same.

Example, If you were to find the squair Root of 576. Suppofing it the squair of Fig. 18. Make first a dash at every other Figure, beginning allwayes at the first towards the right hand *viz.* at 6. and 5. that just so many Figures will be in the quotient or Root; then say, what is the Root of 5. answer, 2. is the nearest, therefore write 2. in the quotient and multiply the same, saying 2 times 2 is 4. write down that under the 5 and substract it therefrom, saying, 4 from 5 there remains 1. thus have you 20 the squair Root of G. *i.c.f.* (considering that there is yet one Figure to follow *)* and now you want the squair Root of the two oblong squairs, *viz. a.b.* G. *h.* and *e.b.f.d.* (out of which you must substract the little squair *e.b.i.h.*) therefore double your quotient or Root of the squair G. *i.c.f.* saying 2 times 2 is 4 write this down for your divisor one Figure foreward *viz.* under 17. and use common division, saying how often can we get 4 out of 17. answer, 4 times, write that in the quotient and say, 4 times 4 is 16. that substracted from 17. remains 1. thus have you 4 the Root of the oblong squair, out of which substract the little squair once, because you have it twice by the former doubling the oblong squair; therefore multiply the side of the little squair, *viz.* 4 in it self, that makes 16. substract the same from 16

　　11
　576(24
　446　⁝
　1.

and

and there remains nothing : so 24 is the squair Root or side *a. b.* whose squair is 576.

Example 2. If the squair of this plot be 543169. make the dashes, as before, *viz.* under 9.1.4. and say, what is the squair of 54. (the dashes so directs, and not to 5. therefore mind the usefullness of them) now the nearest squair Root of 54 is 7. But as in division, so you must look, if you will get the double thereof out of the remainders and the little squair too : If you mind this you cannot go wrong. But upon tryall I find it will so work, therefore set 7 in the quotient and multiply the same, it makes 49 write that down under 54. substract,

```
        13
       204
      15124
     543169 (737
     494969
       1144
```

and there remains 5. This tells that the Root of the large squair is 700. (considering that there is yet 2 Figures to follow as appears by the 3 dashes) now double your quotient, that makes 14 (this is the length of the two oblong squairs) place the same, as in division, and say, how often can we get 14 out of 53. answer 3 times and, 11 remaining ; now substract the little squair whose side is 3. Thus, 3 times 3 is 9. from 111. remaines 102. There is the Root of other two oblong squairs wanting : therefore double the whole quotient *a. b.* 73 that makes 146. place the same as before, for division, and say, how often can we get 146 out of 1026, or gradually, how often one in 10. we get 9 ones in 10, but not 9 fowers in 12 which will remain. then try if we can have 8. No, therefore take 7 and set in the quotient, as before in common division, *viz.* 7 times one from 10. remains 3. and 7. fowers from 23. remains 4. and 7 sixes from 46. remains 4. lastly substract the little squair, *viz.* 7 times 7 from 49. there remains nothing. So the squair Root of 543169. is 737.

And if the Number be never so great, you may observe that the first operation consists of 3 parts. (*i e.* first, finding the Root of the great squair; secondly, the Root of the oblongs by doubling the quotient and using common division; Thirdly, substracting the little squair for the reasons above demonstrated.) The second operation (if there be more than one as in this last example) consists of

2 parts

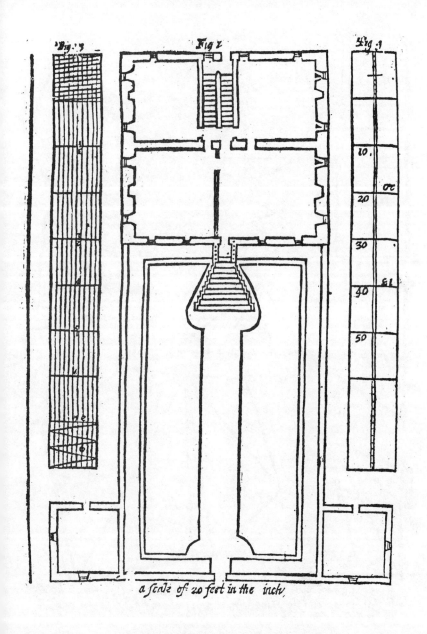

Fig. 3

Fig. 1

Fig. 4

10

20

30

40

50

a scale of 20 feet in the inch

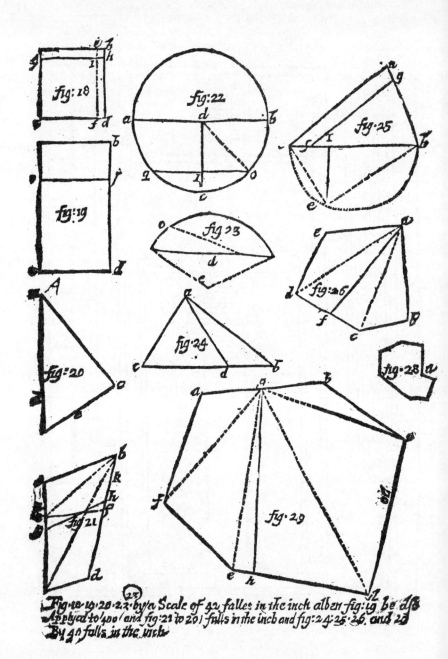

Fig: 18

Fig: 19

Fig: 20

Fig: 21

Fig: 22

Fig: 23

Fig: 24

Fig: 25

Fig: 26

Fig: 28

Fig: 29

23

Fig: 18. 19. 20. 22. by a Scale of 42 falles in the inch albe 21 fig: 19 be dfs
Applyed to 400 and fig: 21 to 201 falls in the inch and fig: 24. 25. 26. and 23
By 40 falls in the inch

Fig: 5   Fig: 6   Fig: 7

Fig: 8   Fig: 9

Fig: 5 6 7 and 8 By a Scale of 92 Ell in the Inch fig: 9. 10 11 12 13 14 15 20 and 19
By a Scale of 84 Ell in the Inch

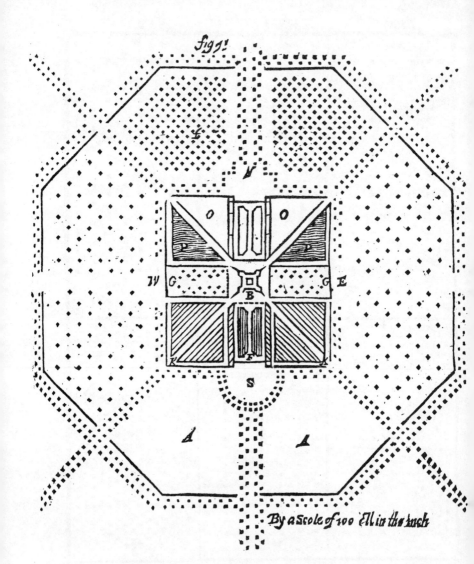

fig 1.

By a Scole of 100 Ell in the inch

2 parts *viz.* firſt the doubling the whole quotient for your diviſor, by which you divide your dividend, as in common. Secondly the ſubſtracting the little ſquair; (whereof the laſt Figure in the quotient is allwayes the Root) and hencefurth in every operation, if never ſo many, you muſt allwayes now proceed as in this ſecond operation.

But to find the ſquair Root of a Number conſiſting of whole Numbers and Fractions, as 930.25 the ſquair of fig. 18. work as if all were whole Numbers, as before, untill one Figure of your diviſor come under the Fraction of your dividend, and then the reſt of the quotient is Fraction, as in the Example is plain.

$$930.25(30.5$$
$$960\ 05$$
$$6\ 2$$

But to find the Root of a Number, that is not a ſquair Number, as 19. ſower is the neareſt, and there remains 3. now, how to know the denominator of this Numerator, is to double the quotient and add one to it, and that is allwayes the denominator to any Fraction happening in Roots; here the Root of 19 is $4\frac{3}{9}$.

$$19(4\tfrac{3}{9}$$
$$16$$

I have given you the Geometricall demoſtration of the ſquair Root, which ſhewes the reaſon of its Arithmeticall operation; and this I could never find in any Book.

I confeſs I need to Apologize for theſe and the like digreſſions, but the earneſt deſire of ſeveralls forced me.

Place the Figures here.

I THE

THE SECOND PART
Of the
SCOTS GARD'NER,
Treating of the Culture of Plants.

CHAP. I.

Of the several wayes of propagation.

I Am not to discribe the varieties in the Tribes and Kindreds of Plants, (seeing I am not now writing a Herbal) but only what is most material to their propagation and improvement: wherefore I shall shew,

First in general the several wayes of propagation, and then particulary some of the most usefull.

2. The several wayes of increasing them are.

First by seeds, Kyes, Kirnells, Nuts, Stones.

Secondly by off-sets, Suckers, Slivings taken from the mother-Plant.

Thridly by Cuttings, Stems, Slips set without Roots.

Fourthly by laying the branch of a growing Plant down into the Earth.

Fifthly by carrying up soil to it, where it will not bend down.

Sixthly by various wayes of Graffings.

Lastly by several wayes of Inoculation.

The

The bufinefs of this Chap : is to fhew the manner and time of performing each of thefe wayes.

3. And firft by feeds, choice them from the faireft Plants, full ripe, the day fair, and Plants dry. Lay them in the Sun and open air a little; fome for Rubbing out, others for winning in their husks. And as you fhould not fow Fruits, Kirnels, Nuts, or Stones with the Flefhy part on, (but eat or Rub it off by Rolling in fand, and then dry them a little) fo nor wafh, Weet, or fteep them. Neither keep any long after they ripe, the moft part will keep till fpring, but then many will ly till the next, efpecially ftony Seeds, Berries, and Kirnells. I do not mean, *Afh*, *Holly*, *Yew*, *Mezeriom*, *Hawthorn*, &c. Who naturally lies a year longer, albeit fowen Immediatly when gathered, yet even fome of thefe namely the holly will ly fometimes a year longer than their ufuall time, if the flefhy part be not Rubbed off.

I might fay fomething of the timely Interring Tulips and others, but I come to the manner of fowing: which is,

To cover the feed with the mould, whereof there is feveral modles according to the nature of the feed, Soil, feafon, or fancy either to fow the Ground and turne the feed in under the furrow, or by drawing trenches in the foil, and then drawing the earth over them with a haw, or fowing the bed ready dreft and hacking in the feed with the fame Inftrument, or by Harrowing, Raking with a Rake or drawing bufhes over the fowed Ground to cover the feed, or to put off the furface of the whole bed with the Rake head and fow thereon, then draw on the mould again with the fame, and having caft up the furrows with a fhovell, fmooth the bed with the Rake, or make drills by lines in made up beds, fow and cover the fame with the Rake head, not diffordering the Ranks, or to fet the fingle feeds with fticks by lines, or to fow the bed, and then to fift fine mould thereon, &c.

Sow the ftrong and hardy deeper than the fmall and tender, and fow ebber at fpring than before winter, and deeper in a light, than a ftiff foil.

Albeit

Albeit I ufe for the moft part to Plant and fow every fpecies by themfelves, yet you may fometimes ufe mixtures, as Carrots and Radifh in one bed, becaufe the Radifh may be gone e're the Carrots require much Room. Among new fet Liquorifh fow Onyons, Radifh, Lettice, and you may fow Radifh, Lettice, Parfly, Carrats, Parfneeps together, gathering each in their feafons, the Parfneeps will ftay till winter. And drop Beat-Rave or parfly in your onyonbeds to ftay winter after onyons ar gone. Alfo Beat-Rave, Skirrets, Beans, at confiderable diftance in the Intervalls of new Planted Artichocks, alfo at a great diftance among cabbages, or in the edge of the furrows of other beds.

The moft naturall time for fowing is, when the feeds of their own accord falls into the ground, neverthelefs that many doth well at this feafon, as ftony feeds and fuch as can endure winter, yet the tender which ar many with us, doth beft in the fpring, but for convenience we fow at feverall other feafons, as in fummer, (at which time they require watering and fhade) and in Autumne (which is the only feafon for fome) who if tender requires defence & fhelter; nor can we have others early at fpring without hot beds, which is required in fpeciall by fuch as comes not to perfection in our fhort Summer.

Endeavour to fow when the foil is in good temper, a hot-furrow is good, but fome grounds will not harrow or Rake when new delv'd or Plow'd, which when expofed fometime to air, Froft, Sun, and Showres doth crumble and fall tender; hence ought fuch to be prepared by fallowing. See more particularly the manner and feafon for each fort in their refpective Chapters following.

4. Suckers ar thefe which growes, Runs, Springs off, or about the mother-Plant, whereof is made off fetts by fevering or parting them off therefrom.

Take off thefe on Trees and fhrubs with a violent but cleanly pull, be carefull of bulbo roots and Anemonies, that you wound not the mother-Plant.

To force fuch as are unapt to put forth Suckers naturally, you

I 3

may

may bair the Root, (of these of a woody substance,) cut it into the pith, slit it down a little, and put in a stick to keep the gap open; level in the earth again : so shall that lip raised spring, (and so much the better if there was an eye immediatly below the cut.) When the branches are grown, cut off this Plant to live by it self.

Another way is to cut the Root through a little distance from the Tree, with a cleanly slop down-wards, and raise up the butt-end of the Root, so cut off till it be a little above the surface, as for Root graffing hereafter discribed, level in and trade the Earth again: so shall the piece left at the Tree send furth young Roots, and the Root so cut and raised send out a Top.

Better Earth for Bulbs and other Roots, will assist them to put forth Suckers.

Cutting the Tops of Fibrous Rooted-herbes, in growing-time will help them to offsets, and to last long too.

The season for severing offsets of Hardie-trees that lose the leaf, is latter end *October* and beginning *November*, albeit you may also any time till *March*, weather open.

Young Tender-trees, with Hardie-greens, let the winter frost be over, and before the sap rise, *April* best for greens.

Bulbo and Tuberous Roots, when they have done springing *i. e.* their stalkes and leaves beginning to wither.

All Fibrous Rooted-herbes, when springing and before they run up to Flower, albeit you may Plant many after the Flower is past, Stalkes and leaves cut, and they springing a Fresh. But the first spring is best.

If drought, Water Shrubs, and Fibrous Rooted Plants, upon their first Planting, at least shade from the Ensuing scorchings, by covering the surface with some vegitable or leitter and Water through the same if needful.

And though you must Water Tubro, and Bulbo Roots, in drought once in two three dayes; yet be sparing, and defend them from too much Raines.

5. To

5. To propagate by cuttings, is to cut off the branch or stem of a Plant, and to set it in the Earth without Roots.

Strip it of leaves and branches, Plant deeper than these with Roots, and in a rich and moist soil, keeping it watered and shaded, Untill Rooted; cut off their Tops save Greens, as if your cutting be 12 Inches long, let 9 be under, and 3 above ground.

The better to effect their Rooting, (if a hard substance, as Yew, Quince, &c.) Twist there ends a little or cleave them a piece: If tender Plants of great Pith as Jasmines, July-flowers, &c. Cut only at a joynt or knot, and plant them: If large stems of Pithy Trees, as Poplars &c. Sharp their ends down to a point, reserving the bark whole on one side.

If stock July-flowers, slit the Bark near the end in several parts round the Stem, fold up the Bark so cut, and taking the peel'd part close off, Plant the same with this Bark spread as you do a Root.

The time of planting cuttings is, (if Trees & Shrubs,) a little before they Spring, and if Herbes, when springing, as above for off-sets: and let the Stems of July-flowers, and Wall-flowers be well shot i. e. something firme, and take such as has not had a Flower.

6. To increase by laying is to bend down some branch to the ground, and with a hooked stick thrust into the ground, stay the same in its place, and cover with earth of deepness as you see fit: let the soil be good, watered and shaded in drought, and from scorching Sun sheltered in Winter, if needfull.

To force their Rooting (if July-flowers) Prune off the under and withered leaves, and cut it at a joynt into the pith (i. e. half way through) and slit it up to the next joynt, thrust down the cut part Gently into the ground, making it fast, cover as before. If Trees and Shrubs, prick the rind full of holes at the place interred, or cut away the Bark round at the same place: but if the branch be small, use it as July-flowers, and if any refuse, ty them hard and fast above the slit with a piece Pack-threed or Wyre, to stop the sap in its course, that it may provide for Rooting. Cut off all their Tops as
you

you lay them, except Greens and some very Pithy Trees.

The time for laying all Trees and Shrubs that lose the leaf, is *October*, as also *March*, if secured from drought. All Greens in *April*, which therefore must be shaded. July-flowers in *March* *April*, or *July*.

The Trees and Sherubs will be Rooted that time twelve moneths at which time transplant them. the July-flower layed in *March* may be transplanted in *July*, or if layed in *July* transplanted next *March* or *April*.

7. Ciruomposition is in all cases, as laying, save only that the earth must be raised up to the branch, becaufe it will not bend down to it. Therefore fasten a Pot, Basket, old Hatt or the like on the Tree (by a stake or some supporter) let it have a hole in its bottome, through which you must put the branch to be propagated, and then fill the Pot with rich earth, (having ordered the branch as before to caufe it Root) and Water it often; willow earth or Rotten willow sticks at the bottom of the Pot helps to retain the moistuer. I have effected this with clay and Cowes dung well mixt (after part of the Bark has been taken off round) clapt about with a double or triple swadling of Straw, or Hay Roaps.

This is a midsummer as well as Spring-work, and very notable for to propagate such as can scarcely be otherwayes obtain'd.

8, Graffing is to take a cyon or twig of a tree and place into another (call'd the stock) fit to receive the same that the inward Bark, or rind of Both may Joyn & saps unite, &c. Whereof there be several wayes, as,

First of Graffing in the clift, saw off the head of the stock in a smooth place, about half a foot above ground, for Dwarffs and Wall-trees ; as also for Standard, Aple, and Pear, (for they will shoot up for a body) but betwixt 3 and 4 foot for Standard-cherrie, and Plum. Pare smooth its head Ragled by the sow, then cleave it a little befide the pith, and with your Pen-knife cut away any jags, roughnefs, or blacknefs that remaines after cleaving on each fide the clift within; then prepare the graff by cutting on both fides

from

from fome knot or bud in forme of a wedg fuitable to the clift with little fhoulderings, not Ragling the end: for if the bark be raifed at the tail or lower end of the graff, *(* efpecially the Cherrie *)* Impeds its growing, cut off its Top about 2 Inches above the fhoulderings clofe behind a leaf-bud; then open the clift with the Graffing Iron, fet the graff *(* or two Graffs if the ftock be great *)* in the clift, fo as the inward part of the rind of the Graff may joyn exactly & clofe to the inward part of the Bark of the ftock, and if it Pinch, as great ftocks will, ty it not as you muft do the fmaller: or put in a little wedg Gently to keep it, take a Slice-bark (from the cut-off head) and cut a hole therein, as it may flide on, & joyn round the butt of the Graff, and cover the ftock clofe over in forme of a hawks hood. laftly cover with clay tempered with Horfe-dung, that hath a little fhort leitter in it, or with foft wax for fmaller ftoks: this is to preferve it from cold & drying-winds, and from wet which harms moft.

Note, if the ftock ftand perpendicular, fet the Graff on the Weft-fide: if not, then place it on the upperfide: if you fear winds fupport them with fticks as Splinters to a broken bone.

Unbind, when you find their bands harme them, towards midfummer, at which tyme top fuch as has fhot fo large as to be in danger of breaking with the winds, efpecially them Graffed in the Bark, hereafter difcribed.

Pull up Suckers, clofe and cleanly from the Roots: alfo Rub off buds that appear on the ftock. Graffs cannot thrive or profper, if the ftoks be uncleanly or illthriving, and this is occafion'd through bad training.

Another way of clift-Graffing is, to cleave the Graff and not the ftock. Thus: prepare the ftock and Graff as for fhouldering *(* next difcribed, *)* then with the Pen-knif, cleave the inward face of the Graff in the cut part, and cut up the ftock with a flop, fo that one lip of the clift-cyon may by bound on the one fide of the ftock, and the other longer lip on the outfide, as in fhouldering.

The Graff fits here, as on a fadle, with a leg on each fide the ftock,

　　　　　　　　　K　　　　　　　　　　　and

and therefore will better refift the Winds; as alfo the wound caufed by the clift, will foon recover. I have them wholly healed the fame year, wherein I Graffed them.

Shouldering is to cut off the head of the ftock, and fmooth it, as at firft; then cut the Graff from a knot, or bud on one fide floping about ane Inch and half long, with a fhoulder, but not deep, that it may reft on the head of the ftock. the Graff muft be cut from the fhoulder fmooth and even, floping gradually, that the lower end be thin: place the fhouldering on the head of the ftock, and mark by the end of the cut part of the Graff, and cut away fo much Bark of the ftock as the Graff did cover; then place both together, that the cut parts of both may joyn and faps unite one on the other: bind them clofe together with bafs, and hood them with clay tempered with dung or wax, as before.

Graffing in the Bark may be ufed in greater ftocks, or in regraffing of old trees, and is only for aples; becaufe later in performing, which may be the latter end *April*, when the Bark of the ftock will peel: for when both ftock and Graff is prepared, (as in fhouldering) inftead of cutting away fome Bark of the ftock; for receiving the Graff you muft flit it on the South-fide from the top allmoft as long, as the floped part of the Graff, and loofen the Bark at the top of the flit with the point of the half round wedg, (made a purpofe tapering down-wards to a point) which alfo thruft down between the Bark and ftock, to make room for the Graff; but firft cut a little Bark at the thin end of the flope of the *Cyon*, that it double not in going doun, yet leave it with a fharp edg; and becaufe when the *Cyon* is put in, it will bear the Bark hollow from the ftock nick or flit, the Bark on each fide the cyon, fo that it may fall clofe to the ftock and to the edges of the cyon; then bind and cover, as before.

Graffing by approach, is good for thefe that holds not well otherwayes: but herein the ftocks muft be placed fo near the Tree, (where the graffs are)that the branch may reach it;then may you clift or fhoulder-graff the twig yon mean to propagate, into the ftock; and as foon as graff and ftock do unite and ar incorporated together,

cut

cut off the cyon or graff underneath, close to the graffed place, that it may subsist by the stock only.

Root-graffing is, to take the twig of any Tree you mean to propagate, and a piece Root of the same kind (cut and Raised up a little as in sect 4.) and graff them by shouldering, uniting the buttends of graff and Root, causing the rind of the Root Joyn to the rind of the graff, and so bind them: the next year they may be Transplanted to nurserie; these will be easily dwarffed, & readily hold, beside that the defect of Stocks ar supplyed, and they fit for transportation.

There be many other wayes, but these nam'd ar the most material.

The time of graffing is, when the sap beginnes to stirr in the spring; you must begin earlier with Cherries, Plumes, some later with Pears, ending with Aples.

Choise not your graffs from such Trees as ar ill-Bearers, neither from such as has not come to bear at all, but from constant and well bearing Trees, and the fairest and fullest of buds thereon : let them have a piece of the precedent years shot, whereof make the tail and shouldering Immediatly below the butt of young wood; and if the stock be large, make the graffs wholly of the lasts years shot; and such (having blowing buds actually upon them) I have seen bear fruit the same year. But some old bearing Trees yields no graffs: wherefore you may cut out some great branch, that it may shoot anew, or rather take off the same branch by circumposition and plant; the which new Tree may furnish you with graffs. Cut your graffs e're they sprout, and keep them or carry them, their ends in clay, or dry in a box, their tops cut off.

9. Inoculation differs from the former wayes of graffing, and most proper for Apricoks and peaches : any sort will more readily hold by this than by graffing, except Cherries; they come quickly to be a Tree : for I had a plum shoot above 6 foot, 10 Inches the first year; and thô they miss, yet the stock is not the worse. Therefore.

In

In fome convenient and fmooth part of the ftock (at the fame hight as for graffing) with the penknife cut the rind overthwart, and from the midle thereof gently flit the bark about an Inch long in forme of. *a T*, not wounding the ftock; then nimbly prepare the bud by cutting off the leaf till a little of the tail, then flit the bark on each fide a little diftance from the bud, and about half Inch above and below the fame, fharp that end below that it may the more eafily go down, and having a quill, cut more than half away about an Inch long at the end, (for dividing the bud and rind from the ftalk) therewith take it off dextroufly and leave not the Root behind: for if you fee a hole under the bud on the infide, the Root is gone, caft it away and prepare another. when the bud is ready, then with a bone (made half round and fharp at the point tapering on the one fide) raife the bark or rind on each fide the flit carefully, not hurting the inner rind, and with care put in the bud, thrufting it down till its top Joyn with the crofs cut: then bind it clofe above and below the bud with dry'd Rufhes or bafs. Or,

You may flit the bark of the ftock upwards from the crofs cut. Or,

Cut the edges of the bark about the bud oblong fquair, and the bark of the ftock fit to receive the fame. Or

Referve $\frac{1}{4}$ of this fquair piece bark of the ftock untaken off at the upper end, which muft be raifed, that the fhild may flide up betwixt the fame and the ftock; and fo bind gently, as before.

The time for Inoculation is, when the fap is moft in the ftock, namely from *June* till *Auguft*, neer a moneth after unbind *i. e.* cut through binding and bark with a gentle flit on the back fide of the ftock, leaving the binding to fall away of its own accords: at which-time you will fee who holds. In *March* following, cut off the head of the ftock 4 Inches above the bud, and that time twelve moneths the ftub too, that it may heal over the wound. you may prune as graffes, and pull up fuckers &c. See Chap: 4. for more.

Choife buds from good bearers, as before, take them from the ftrong and well growen fhoots of the fame year, and from the biggeft end of the fame, and if you muft carry them farr, firft cut off
their

their leaves, and top of the Stalks and wrap them in moist leaves or grafs.

This much at prefent in general for time and manner of the feveral wayes of propagation.

16. In planting all plants prune their Roots, that is, Top them a little with a fharp Knife except Afparagus. Alfo cut their heads except Greens, and Tops of Forreft-trees ordain'd for Timber, yet the Side-boughes muft, that the head may be proportion'd to the Root.

Plant no Trees deep;(albeit fome deeper than other) when their Roots runs near the furface, there they receive the beneficial influence of Sun and Showres, that makes vegetables fair and Fruitfull.

Lay leitter or the like above ground the Compafs of their Roots, efpecially the firft year of planting. and indeed all plants require fome fhelter & fhade with Moifture, when firft planted, till they get Rooting and ftrength

Cut the leaves and ftalks of flowers and herbes, when paft flower or yealded feed, nor at any tyme fuffer too many, rather purge them in tyme. no more branches, flowers, fruits on any tree, or plant, than the root can nourifh perfectly.

Neither plant and fow every year the fame plants, on the fame Ridg or Bed: for it Improves them to be changed. fee more fully planting, pruning, preferving, &c. in their refpective places following.

K 3

CHAP.

CHAP. II.

How to Cultivate, and prepare grounds.

1. HAving shew'd the several wayes of propagating plants, it is also most requisite that you prepare the ground for effectuating the same. And that is in the first place,

To trench it, *viz.* Begin at one end of the ground, (you mean thus to culture and open) a trench from one side to the other, thereof 3 or 4 foot broad, and from one to two foot deep, as the qualitly of the ground admits and plants require (therefore liquorish must have deeper,) this being open, measure off other 4 foot parallel at its side, turne that into the open trench, with the turf or surface in the bottome, and the clean earth on the top; the filling whereof emptieth another, therefore cut off other fower foot and turne that in as before; thus trench by trench till the whole be finshed. I presume you carryed the earth of the first trench to fill the last, or otherwayes filled hollowes therwith, and left the last trench open, (if convenient) for receiving weeds. Or if the ground be hollow in the midle begin there, and trench both wayes to help the level; if high in the midle, begin at both sides or ends till the two open trenches meet at the hight, for the same reason.

The latter end of harvest the ground is softest for trenching, and it lying all Winter open to the weather is thereby meliorated. For as trenching doth well prepare hard, barren, and untoil'd ground, se doth it such as is exhausted by long and unskilfull usage. and if at every trenching you apply proper manures mixt with the second spading, or under the last shovelling, and in 5 years retrench, it will become to your wish, for all gardens, and plantations.

2. The next excellent way of preparing ground, is fallowing; begin as soon as you reap the crop, but let the ground be something
thing

thing moiſt, albeit you ſhould ſtay for a ſhowre, if this be not late in Autumne, you may fallow in *November*: eſpecially if ſtiff ground and reſtirre in *March* or *April* when you plant or ſow; and albeit you ſhould neither plant or ſow it that year, keep it clean of weeds in ſummer by hawing, &c. and at Autumne fallow again. but as in trenching ſo in this work you ſhould mix with proper ſoil.

Make uſe of the *Engliſh* faſhion of ſpades which are now common, and let every two delvers, have a ſhoveller to caſt up the ſmall that falls in bottom of the furrow, and the Delvers ſhould turne up the point of the ſpade, and nimbly break and chop all the clods throughly; this is very material as well as the through mixing of the manures with the ſoil: So that mixing, ſtirring, reſtirring, fallowing is moſt pertinent for the cold, chilled, barren Rugged-natur'd-ground in *Scotland* all which ſoftens and tenders it, and ſo fits it for nouriſhing good ſeed and plants, as I can tell by experience, therefore.

3. I adviſe our Husband-men alſo to the fallowing of their land, as one; flitfolding the ſame, as a ſecond; Watering, or overflowing land, as a thrid, burning the Turf as a fourth, draining exceſſive moiſture, as a fifth; applying proper ſoils and manures, and that at proper ſeaſons, as a ſixt; laying the land to reſt, as a ſeventh; and above all, incloſing and planting about their land, as the laſt, and beſt improvement.

Example : At the Autumnal fallowing, delve, or Plow deep, and apply hot unrotted and uncompound dungs and manures : at ſpring re-plow or re-delve, and apply ſuch dungs and manures as has layn mixed and rotted with Earth; then Mix, Rake, or Harrow. The ſummer following is to deſtroy the weeds, and may be done by Turf, Plough or by hawing.

The Huſhbandmens flitfolding is equivalent to Gard'ners covering the ſurface, eſpecially of dry and barren ground with leitter, &c. The dung and urine of Sheep and cattle waſhes evenly into ground, and ſhould be turned down by the ſummer,

and

and Autumnal fallowing , left its substance exhaust by Sun and Air, (except that for grafs, then only harrowed with a bush of thorns) instead whereof Gard'ners should top their coverings of leitter with a little Earth or Sand, and at Autumne delve all down together.

Husbandmens watering is by Running Plough-furrowes (and trenches where needful) alongst or crofs their land, fo as the water may gently fweem over the whole: this in the Winter, on dry and barren grounds, which leaves Sulphureous pinguidity behind it, and ftrongly improves either for grafs or corn; but that this Husbandry ought as well to be practifed on wet grounds, is evident, that the Running of this carryes away the fowr quality of the other. I shall fpeak of Gard'ners watering more particularly.

Burning land is, to pare its furface with the Turf Plough and lay the fame in heaps to burn; and fo fpreads the ashes: but if mofs and heath, fet fire through, without turfing it; this deftroyes the noxious fowr nature and the falt remains in the ashes, for the ftrengthening the Spirit of the Earth.

Draining the wet, bogie or dropfical ground is, by trenches a little deeper than the Spring, (how deep foever) and then apply lyme, foot, ashes, pigeons dung, &c. As for the abounding of fuperficial water, that is eafily helped by common waterfowers, or in fome grounds by finking holes down to the channel.

As the Husbandman should have his land layed out or divided into feveral clofes, fome for corn, fome for medow, and others for pafture: fo when he has taken 5, 6, or 7 crops of corn, he should lay it out for pafture, otherwayes it will wear out of heart; and likwayes the pafture muft be plowed up for corn, efpecially when it beginnes to grow moffie.

The way that the Gard'ner turns his ground to reft, is by trenching and retrenching, whereby it can never wear out: albeit he alfo obferves to change the crops as well as the Husbandman.

How

How to Inclofe and plant about your land fee Chap. 4.

4. Among all the Varieties of foils, that next the furface of them is beft, becaufe prepared by the Influence of Sun and Showers,

That called a loam or light brick Earth is the moft natural ground for gardens and plantations; ftrong Blew, White, or Reid clayes are worft : but the nearer they be to a mixture of loam (or if they have ftones naturally in them) they ar the better; alfo, the nearer gravelly or fandy grounds incline to loam, fo much the better. therefore if your ground be ftiff, trench with ferns, ftraw, bean-ham, thatch, leitter, Earth under woodftacks, fmall fticks, &c. If gravelly or fandy, then trench and mix with loam or the upper part of clay, the Turf of both is good.

If ftrong clay, trench and mix with fat fand, highway Earth that hath drift fand in it, Rubifh of buildings, Lime-Rubifh, gravel. And if it be for gardens or orchards, enrich it with dungs mixt with drift-fand or light mouldheaped up *ftratum fuperftratum i. e.* laying by laying. And if the ground be cold, the more pigeons and poultrie dung you put in it, the lighter and warmer it will be. Or make *Stratums* of Earth, dung and unflaked limeftones to ly a year, and then apply this compofition, which has been hitherto a great fecret: therefore prize it.

Binding grounds, which will not Rake as you delve, if dry and hard, trenching and fallowing expofeth them to be foftned by weather, as is faid: But if wet and tough, mix with Afhes, fea-Sand, &c. In Culturing.

For preparing my compofts, I ufe a pit (wherein fomtimes I make a hot-bed) oblong, about 4 foot deep of length and breadth, as I can get dungs, Vegetables, and foils to fill it: here to lay all Kindes or forts with *Stratums* of Earth, as horfe, neat, Sheep, Pigeons, and Poultrie dung, ferns, weeds, leaves, foot, afhes, fticks, faw-duft, feathers, hair, horns, bones, urine, fcouring of pondes, ditches, blood, pickle, brine, fea-water, the the cleanfing of Houfe of Office, &c. Let them ly a year at leaft,

L

but

but not above two: then take them out and there Stirre, Air, mingle and work them with fresh Earth or by themselves, as you have occasion, till they become sweet and of an agreable scent; (yet retaining their vertue) this frees them from the noxious qualities they otherwayes retaine, and consequently not so apt to gender or produce Worms, Weeds, and Mushroms in-stead of wholsome and pleasant plants, fruits, and Roots for the table.

5. Observe what manures are proper for the soil, as, all hot-dungs and manures are proper for cold, stiff, and moist grounds : so all rotten and cold dungs and manures are proper for dry and hot gro-unds. All manures that retaines moisture are for poor, Sandy and Gravelly soils

As, Horse-dung for stiff and cold ground; Sheeps for hot and dry; Ashes for cold, stiff and moist; old Woolen-rags for poor dry; Lyme most excellent for moorish and heatly land ; Hair of Beasts for dry and stiff grounds ; pigeons and poultrie dung for cold and moist; Rotten saw dust for dry ; Rubish of buildings for stiff, cold grounds ; Salt for cold and moist ; use it moderately it destroyes vegetables on dry ground, especially at first, but when melted by Winter Raines, it fertilizeth: Some has sowen it on moist, moorish land to great advantage, for being farr from the Sun we have little volatile.

6. In your applications you are to consider, that Rotten dungs and manures are proper for Trees and such slow growing plants, and unrotten dungs and manures for Annualls, they being quick of digestion.

Let not the Root of any Tree stand on dung, farr less unrotten dung which burns them; but upon prepared and proper soil, and composed, well mixed, aired, stirred or fallowed. Most fit is the clean-sings of streets and highwayes together, with the mud and scouring of pondes and ditches, if first layed on heaps in the open Air to rott and sweeten, and if you mix it with stratums of Lyme that adds much to its goodness and fertility.

Forrest.

Forreſt-trees require not ſo much dung as Fruit-trees, but well mixed and fallowed ſoil.

Kitchen Herbes and Roots requires very fat, light, warme and well cultured ground.

Flowers and fine plants cannot endure ſoil too rank with dung, neither can they proſper if it be poor; but freſh, clean Earth with rotted neats dung well beaten and mixed together, and a little rotten willow Earth a little below the Roots : here comes in that delicate ſoil, the Turf of the paſture mixt with a little Lyme, Cowes and Sheeps dung, well rotted and mingled as before. See more particularly what ſoil each kind or ſort of plants delights in or loves beſt, in their reſpective Chapters and Sections following.

7. As for making the hot-bed for raiſing early and tender plants, dig a pit (4 foot deep, and of length and breadth, as you have occaſion) in a convenient and warme place, lying well to the Sun and ſheltered from winds (which you may help by art, if not ſo naturally) fill it with dung and leitter from the Stables, about a fourthnights gathering, (ſome makes it of Barley-ſtraw, or the ſame mixt with bran, becauſe it keeps heat long, and its heat not ſo exceſſive nor ſo noiſome to plants as dung) and when well Tread, and even on the Top, lay about 4 Inches thick of rich, light (but freſh and clean) ſifted mould thereon : arch it over with ſticks, and cover with matts 4 or 5 dayes to cauſe it heat, then uncover and give it Air a day or two, that its violent heat may paſs; then ſow your ſeeds and cover the bed again And the next day if you find the bed over hot give it more Air, if too cold caſt ſome Straw on the covering untill the heat returne; ſo by airing and covering you may keep it in a conſtant temper : when the Seeds come up, give them Air to dry the moiſture raiſed by the heat of the bed. How to cover the choice with Glaſſes, ſee Chap. 6. Sect, 1. But as there is great trouble in rightly ordering this ſort of hot-bed; ſo here remedied by a better, which is only to fill and tread the pit full of new dung and leitter, (not covering it with Earth) and place wooden caſes therein, about 9 or 10 Inches deep and about 3 foot broad, (having wood-handles

at

at the ends) boar them full of Auger or Wimble holes at the bottome, fill them with the forefaid earth; and therein fow your feeds: and thefe cafes and the earth in them will be kept warme during the whole feafon, wherein a hot-bed is neceffary. for if it lofe heat add frefh dung and leitter under, about and betwixt the cafes; (there is Dew on the Glaffes, while the heat remains, but if exhaufted, they will be dry) confequently the trouble of tranfplanting from one hot bed to another is hereby faved. Provide a fhelter over the whole, if you pleafe, and frames of Glafs over fome of the infide cafes, where there is moft need; others you may leave open, as your Seeds requires. By this your pit and cafes are every year ready to your hand, requiring only a fupply of frefh dung. But this pit will be fo much the more excellent, if lyn'd round at the fides with brick: and where you cannot conveniently fink it for Water, you may build the fame above ground. And when this pit is empty it will be alfo ready for wintering of Flower Pots with *July-flowers*, &c.

8. In watering plants, ufe not well-water, efpecially for tender plants, neither Rivers that run long and quick on fharp gravel: thefe yields no nourifhment to plants, but rather chills them; therefore if you muft ufe fuch, let them ftand fometime in the Sun and open Air, uncovered in tubs, mixt with dung, and powr it off the dreg when you ufe it. let the quantity and quality of the dung be according to the nature of your plants (as if great growers and require much heat, put horfe or pigeons dung into the water, but for the more durable put Sheeps dung) remembering if your ground be bad, to add the more dung.

When dung lyes above ground about any plants, (as I ufe to do with Trees, Artichocks, &c.) The water defcending through the fame is very relifhing to the Roots, if you powr the water at a little diftance round the Tree: for when lafhed on the ftem, it wafheth the Earth from the Roots.

Water no plants with ftanding, ftinking Ditch-water, nor no Water that ftinketh: Rain-water and large Ponde-water is excellent, but keep it not too long; yet if in a large Veffel, the

of-

oftener you Stir it, the longer it will keep fweet : fo the larger your pondes or Rivers be , and the opener to the Sun and Air, and the more moving by horfe, geefe and ducks their Sweeming, the fweeter it will be. and if the wafhings of ftables, ftreets, dung Hill-water , &c. Run into them , that adds much to their fertility, providing they have fome moving, as is faid, to make them fweet.

If you fear dry weather differre not too long , but water while your ground is yet moift ; differre not, if you mind to water at all. thefe that Root deepeft, water moft. and alfo when you do begin, Continue it fo long, as you find occafion. In watering Trees and greater Plants, ftir and waken the Earth a little about their Roots with a fork, fo as it may drink the more evenlier, minding to tread firme again. And for the fame caufe you may fink the Earth a little in forme of a fhallow difh rownd your Coleflowers, Artichocks, &c. Dip your Flower Pots in a Tub of water, to drink through the holes at the bottome.

When you water beds of fmall feeds with the watering pot, fhake it nimbly, that it may fall like a fhowre of fmal Rain. I have often made ufe of a handful of fmall Straw or Hay drawen as thatch, tyed in the midle, and at one end powred water with a Cup, and fhaked the fame that it appeared like a Gentle bedewing rather than a glutting Rain.

Some that are defirous to have the ground allwayes moift about any plant, do place near it a veffel with water, and in it a piece woollen clothe with one end thereof hanging out to the ground, and the other in the water : the Cloath being firft wet, it will drop continually, if the end without be lower than that within the veffell : and when the water within fails, it may be augmented; If it drop not faft enough, the clothe may be increafed, if too faft, diminifhed.

Early in the Spring while the weather is yet cold, I intreat you be cautious in watering the leaves of the young and tender plants, only wet the ground about them when your plants or feeds are more hardy and the nights yet cold, water in the fore-noons: but when the nights are warme, or dayes very hot, then the evening is the beſt time.

Plant in wet, and ſow in dry. I do not mean over wett or over dry. Withall let them have good Air, which conduceth much to their health and life, without which nothing can live.

CHAP. LII.

How to propagate and order Forreſt-trees.

1. OMmiting here the diſtinction of ſpecies, (having con-fin'd to one chapter) I ſhall ſpeak briefly, yet I hope plainly of their Governement, thus:

Albeit the moſt of Forreſt-trees may be Increaſed by Suckers, Layers, &c. Yet if you deſire Trees worth your while, Raiſe them from the ſeed. Therefore prepare a ſeminary or ſeed-plot together with a nurſerie well ordered and handſomely made up in beds, as in part 1. Chap. 5. ſect. 2. and there ſow and ſet your ſeeds and plants in their reſpective ſeaſons ; keep them clean from weeds, and water them when need is: alſo Earth up and dible in theſe caſt up by the Froſts, as well as ſhade and ſhelter in time of neceſſity. Let them ſtand ſome but one , others two years in the ſeminary after they riſe, then remove and plant in nurſerie , a foot one way and half the other diſtance, or 5 Rowes in the bed (if 6 foot broad,) in ſtraight lines, having firſt prun'd their Roots , eſpecially toped the main Root that runs ſtraight down; ſo ſhall they ſend furth ſyde or feeding Roots, and agree well with tranſplanting thereafter. Alſo proportion the head to the Root by pruning up the ſide boughes, reſerving ſome ſmalleſt afterwards all the way on the body, to ſtop the ſap in its courſe, that the Tree may grow great with its hight, and this will prove the beſt fortification againſt the winds.

Cut

Cut not the tops of these Trees you ordain for Timber, except some grow crooked in the nurserie; these save Greens may be sell'd near ground in the Spring or at midsummer, and train up the streightest shoot again to be the Tree. When they have stood 3 years at most in this nurserie, replant them at a wider distance in Spad-bit trenches, 3 foot one way and two the other, where they may stand till they be ready for planting out in your Avenues, Parks, Groves, &c. Which will be in 3 years, if thir Rules be observed. But if you think them yet too small for setting out, you must transplant at a wider distance, and at every remooval Top all their Roots with a sharp Knife, and thin the side-boughes for lightning the head: but do not prune up all, as is the Custome of the ignorants, whose Trees are so long, small and top-heavy, that they cannot stand; but of pruning more hereafter. It you neglect this transplanting and pruning the top Root, while young, your essayes to do it when old will prove ineffectual, nor will they ever be worth the while.

All the time that your Trees remains in nurserie, and at least the first and second year thereafter, be carefull to cleanse them from Weeds and Suckers by delving, hawing, &c. The advantage here shall soon counter-ballance the cost.

Choice your Seeds from the high, streight, young and well thriving Trees; and the fairest, weyghtiest, and brightest thereon: for its observed that the seeds of hollow Trees (*i. e.* Trees whose pith is consum'd) doth not fill well or come to perfection, as *Langford* sayes of Pears, concluding that the Kirnells of Fruit depend much upon the pith. And I bid you reject such as was never set by art, as Peevish parents for Children, that must be thus accommodat with uncouth lodgings as well as dyets in their travells: Its a mischief in many people that accompts all ridiculous, that they have not been bred up with or accustom'd unto, so with Trees in some respect.

2. As for the Oak, the Acorns we get from　　　　puts furth a lustier shoot than ours; nor do I approve of them in natural woods, they ripe beginning *October*, gather them in a dry day, and lay in some open Room to dry a moneth, turning them with a broom, then

lay

lay them in a couch dry fand till latter end *February*, dible them in the ground 2 Inches deep, 1 2 rowes in the bed, (if 6 foot broad;) they come up the fame feafon, and allthough they will grow on any ground, yet they grow better on the beft, that is a good loamy Earth. Order them as is directed in nurferie.

The Elm that growes with a clean and taper body is beft worthy your care. we have extraordinary clean and fmooth barked Elms from *Holland* : but I think they take more paines in preparing and making their Earth fine, which certainly is moft conducible thereunto. Their Seed falls beginning of *June*, (thô it doth not fill every year) when they begin to fall, gather them and fpread on a Clothe a little, then fow them immediatly promifcuoufly over the bed, and very thick covered near an Inch of Earth; I had them come up within 10 dayes : they love a light Earth fomething moift.

The Afh feed is ripe in *November* and *December* : having fpread them a little to dry, put them in a hole *ftratum*, *fuperftratum* of Earth and Seed ; take them out at Spring come twelve moneths, and fow as Elm, for now they rife ; and loves a tender foil not too moift.

The great Maple, commonly, but falfly called Plan, its feed is ripe in *September*: fow it at Spring it, comes up that feafon : affects a foil with Afh or rather better.

The fmaller Maple is rather for Hedg, its feed lyes as Afh.

The Beach feed ripes the end of fept : but it fills not well every year, nor ar we fo very plentiful of old trees, as could be wifhed: for that caufe we fend abroad for feed. as foon as it comes to our hand, it may be fowen, or rather keept in a couch of fand, as the great Maple till the fpring, for it comes up that feafon: affects a light foil, no clayes.

The Walnuts, and cheftunt, albeit they be fruit trees, I plant them without the orch : walls, their nuts ripes beginning of *Octob* : when they begin to fall take them off and rub off the outward husk, but do not weet them, then order them as accorns ; they come up the firft

fea-

feafon and affects a hight loamy earth. I could wifh for more hor-fechefnuts their feed from turkie.

The black cherrie or green is a tree that I love well in Avenues and thickets. there is a fort at *Niddrie-caftle* where I was born 7. miles weft from *Edinburgh*, whofe fruit is preferrable to any cher-rie : I take it to be a fort of heart, but it's a great bearer; (which pro-pertie the heart cherrie wants) they ar beft ftocks for ftandard cher-ries. learned *Evelen* and Ingenious *Cook* takes notice of this tree.

Gather their fruit wheen full rip, the beginning *Auguft*, eat of the flefhy part *i. e.* the fruit, and lay the ftones to dry a little, then lay them by *ftratums* with earth, which prepares them, if fow'd at fpring to rife that feafon, otherwayes they ly till the next: they affect a light, fharp foil, and if you may, mix it with compoft ; and then it fhall be for cherries of all forts.

The *wild Service*, commonly called Rons-tree, their fruit ripes in *Sept:*which you may eat or Rub off by rolling in fand; then prepare & fow them as cherrie. They love a moift Ground or fhade not wet, if you will plant them in better foil in Avenues, me thinks, they would be very pleafant when fpread over with their umblefafhion'd, bright Red fruit.

The *Line or Lidne* tree, commonly called *Lym*, the broad leafed with odoriferous flowers is beft. the feed ripes beginning *Octob*:But fills not well every year with us, and indeed we have few come to any confiderable perfection; yet I have feen them bear feed at *Ha-miltoun*. it fhould be a little dryed in an open Room and couched in moift fand till winter pafs, and then fow'd in a little fhade, for they muft not be too much expofed to the fcorching Sun: they come up the fame feafon; but if not prepared through winter, they lie till the next. they love a frefh loamie earth (& in planting them I advife you to cover the furface of the earth about them with leitter topt with earth the firft year at leaft.

The *horn beam* may be ordered as fmall *maple* they like a dry ftiff ground, they are copfis.

The *haffell* and filboards feed or nuts is ufed as wallnuts, they de-
M
light

light in dry banks, nor are they stately forrest trees.

The Birch is a proper tree for much of our poor, dry and barren grounds: I never raised any of them by seed in the wood, they are so plentie by suckers, &c. Many of which handsome trees I have planted successfully.

The Beantree soil vulgarly called peascod-tree, its seed ripes in *Oct.* and being kept dry all winter, sown at spring comes up that season, and affects a moist Ground but sweet.

The white poplar vulgarly called *Abele*, its a quick grower and pleasant tree, so is *Aspen*; they are easilie propagated by cuttings; so the last by suckers, see *chap. 1. sect. 5.* They love a good soil something moist.

The *Alder* is so propagable and loves the marshes; and so is

The willowes, Sallows, and oziers, they all affecting a moist ground and must be so kept till Rooted.

But I come to greens; as

The Pinetree and pinasters whose husks you may expose to the sun till they open & seeds fall out, to be sowen in *March* but if late ere they come home (they requiring the summer sun to open them) if you then sow, they cannot get strength sufficient to withstand the ensuing winter; therefore keep them in dry sand all winter, and sow them in the spring; For they rise that season wherein they are sowed, they love a good and tender soil, they are something tender while young, (as all greens are) the great Pine is tenderer than pinasters, and nice in transplanting. therefore observe the Rule in *chap. 7. sect. 2.* Shade and shalter in both extremities of heat and cold while young. But non so proper for us as

The Scots Firre, many one of their husks have I gathered any time between *Jan:* and latter end *March*, lay them on a Cloth to the Sun which opens them, to be sowen latter end *Aprile*, they come up that season, and loves a soil with Pinus. See how to order in nurserie: for they must be dibled in again the first year, as spued up by frosts; they or any Tree will grow on most sorts of grounds if well ordered, and prepared and secured from drought
the

the firft year. And therefore help the ground where its not to purpofe, (they will pay you or yours for your pains) as if you plant in
gravelly or dry fandy ground, mix it with clay and turfe a large
diftance round about the Roots : or if in ftiff and moift clayes,
trench 8 or 9 foot on each fide round the compafs of the Roots, adding fmall gravel, fatt fand, &c. And plant ebb: but enough of
his in the laft Chapter.

The filver Firre is fo ordered, only its tender while young, and
fubjeét to blafting.

The Pitch Tree (as common Firre,) its a hardie Tree, and no wonder, feeing, as I am Informed, it growes by nature plentifully in
Norraway.

The Yew is alfo a hardie Tree, only requires fome defence
while young, their Berries ripes in *Novem:* Rub off the flefh or clam-
my fubftance, and lay them to dry a little, (but not at the fire) then
box them *Stratum Superftratum* of earth and feed, placing them
in the fhade till the fpring come twelve moneths; at which time fow
them, and then they fpring, affeéts a good foil, not ftiff.

The *Holly* is to be ufed as *Yew :* for they ly as long; its the moft
proper for hedges of all the plants in the World. Next thereunto, is
the *Hawthorne* (tho not a green) whofe feed ripes in *Oéfob :* and
to be ufed as Holly : for it rifeth not till the fpring come twelve moneths ; and the better you prepare and mix the ground with Rotted
dung, the larger will they fhoot. Nor let any Imagine, that Holly
alfo loves not dunged ground, nay, (fay they) poor and gravelly
foil; but I know the contrary by experience.

I fhall fpeak of fome fhrubs in Chap: 7. for I muft leave them
here, and come fhew you how to tranfplant and prune the ftately
forrefttrees.

3. In Tranfplanting remove with earth about their Roots (if
you can) efpecially greens, at leaft take all the Roots up a good
diftance from the ftem, by making a Trench round, and be not
haftie : then top all their Roots with a fharpe knife, (flop tending
down as a horfe foot) cut off all the bruifed and broken parts till you

come

come at firme wood, top the small Roots like hair, to make them
stiff, so as they fold not, when the Earth is put in, and rott thereby : proportion the head also to the Root by thinning it, prune side-
boughs; (reserving allwayes some for tapering the Tree) these
you cut, do it close and smooth by the body, slanting upwards,
and they will soon overgrow the wounds, if the branch cut off be
not great. Cut not the tops of *Oaks*, *Beaches* they cannot endure
it, neither any Tree that you ordain for timber; albeit I have been
necessitate to lop great old Trees, whose heads could not otherwayes be conform'd to their Roots, which necessarly ar diminished upon removal. But this is not the case of well trained Trees
in a nurserie.

The Rule for removing old large Trees out of woods or other places, who was never before Transplanted, is to make a trench at two
sides of the Tree, distance considerable, till you can Inforce the Tree
upon on side: then cut the top Root through, saving as many col-
lateral Roots as you can; lessen its head, or lop it if it can suffer, and
so set up the Tree again, and tread in the earth about it, as it was; let
it stand 2 years to emitt fibres or feeding Roots to nurse it when
Planted out.

But to my nursed trees again.When you remove, as is directed, carry
them as quickly to their new quarters as you can; let the soil where
you set them be as *Connatural* to the nurserie as possible, see the last
chap. for preparing grounds and see part 1.*chap.* 3. and 4. for the
orderlie wayes of planting.

The best way is to make the holes a year before you plant, and in
summer stirr and turne their earth, that no weeds grow thereon:
make them betwixt, 12. and 18. Inches deep, and betwixt 4. and
8. foot diameter, if ordinarie trees: but if the ground be bad and not
proper for the trees, then trench, mix & apply, till such become more
agreeable.

When you plant, lay the surface in the bottome and fill up the
hole with fine earth, till it can only admit the upper part of the root to
stand level with the surface, (this is not to plant deep, for they that do;
but

but cheat themſelves) then ſet on the Root of the tree in the midle of the hole, and if no earth adhere to the ſame, make a little hut in the middle of ſmall earth, and lay the roots right ſpread round about with your hands that non ly folded or diſorderly, then put in fine ſmall earth amongſt the roots,& ſhake and move the tree, ſo that the earth may go in amongſt them till no cavity or void be left to let in the air; ſuch roots as folds raiſe up and level in their wonted poſture with your hands ſhovelling on more earth and tread gently, then fill one more and tread well with your heels till it be as farr filled up about as it ſtood in the earth before, make the bulk about level on the top, and juſt the breadth of the hole, and it will be about half a foot above the ſurface if ordinary nurſſed trees and good ground. you may put on the rounding ſtring to make its edges circular and handſome, or if you will to make it like a geometrical ſquair, then ſtreight lines from ſide to ſide of a thicket will make up the bulks that the whole will appear as walks and bordours two wayes: lay new horſe dung and leitter or ferns above the bulk (ſo as it touch not the ſtem) covered with a little earth to keep it from drying, the Rains will waſh in its ſubſtance and refreſh the Roots, beſides it keeps out ſummer drough and winter froſts.

The firſt year at leaſt go through, now and then, and tread them right after winds. I am not for ſtaking trees (but for training them ſo as they may not need it,except you drive three ſtakes about each tree at the out ſide of the bulk, then the double ſtraw Roaps tyed from its body to all the three ſtakes will ſecure; and if you faſten croſs ſticks briers and thorns, here ſhall be a fence about each tree. Rub off buds that offer to break foorth near the Root or any place where you would not have them, (but ſtill leave ſome here and there on the ſide to ſtop the ſap from running too much in head)keep them clean of ſuckers & weeds by hawing in ſummer, & delving & looſening the mould about them ſpring and Autumne *i. e.* at the two equinoxi alls, and tread faſt again, as fearing drought and winds.

Obſerving is what is ſaid, you may expect monamental, clean and well thriving trees,if right prun'd and well Incloſed.

The

The time of planting, see season for off sets Chap. 1. Sect. 4. neglect not your time of early planting, that is, as soon as they give over growing, and before the frosts come on, and you shall see them farr out-strip these set in the Spring, though have often planted in the Spring through necessity, but then I was allwayes something more than ordinary carefull to defend them from the ensuing droughts, by covering their bulks and watering, &c. Yet I preferre the Spring for Firr, and other such Greens, which therefore unavoidably requires the same care.

4. I shewed before how to prune in the nurserie while young, now continue, when planted out whilest they be small, prune every year, when a little older once in 2 years, then once in 3 or 4. and never seldomer than in 5 or 6.

And as you prune up the body, till the desired hight leave small branches here and there by the way, that it may bring greatness with its hight, and be by consequence the more able to stand; let never a Tree get a greater head than its Root is sufficiently able to nurse and bear; neither be Rash in loping them, except they be already top-heavy, which brings crookedness; if so, cut at a crooked place, slanting upwards, clean and smooth, and train up the streightest shoot again to be the Tree : or rather if you can save its head by thinning and croping the branches on that side which leans i. e. the underside, thus at midsummer, and slit the Bark in the Spring, so may it grow streight and taper. Purge still the head when needfull and prune superfluities, cut off all that Cross, Rubs, Frets, and Galls on another. Permit not Trees to Fork, train them with one streight and taper body, and a handsome round Pyramidall head. And when you prune, cut close and smooth by the body or bough with the Knife, or Chissell and Mell, or if the branch be great, cut with a saw (nicking it underneath first) and smooth it with the Chissell, so will it the better heal : but if the Tree be very old and the branches great, such will never be able to overgrow the wound, therefore if you must cut such, do at a little distance from the body, the wound declining the Horizon. Thus Train pines, Firrs, Pitch, and these of the Conicall Tribe in stories only (which
methode

methode they naturally follow , *)* you may cut out some of the greatest branches of the under storie , but so as you leave them regular
or equally furnished round : so may you leave one storie, cut out
the second , leave the thrid , &c. Cut not their tops, yet you
may crop some of their side-boughes if the Tree be top-heavy , and
afterwards as the Tree gets footing , cut these clean off.

There be two seasons for pruning such as lose the leaf : the first
for these of little pith is *October* and *November* , or any time in
Winter : and for them of soft wood and great hearts, and for
Greens let the frosts be over, and before the sap in them rise, except
Firrs and other Rosinious Trees in *November*, because if prun'd
in *March* they bleed , and in *September* and *October* they have not
given over growing.

The second time is midsummer, which is ordinarly about the
end of *June* : this is a safe time to prun them of great pith and any
that is unapt to bleed; but especially for cutting of young shoots
of this year : extripate all such buds and shoots as you desire not
to grow, and hereby you may make clean bodied Trees, albeit
never so apt to break out in Side-boughes, as some Elms are.
for the diseases of all Trees with their cures, see Chap. 5.Sect. 8.
and 9.

CHAP. IV.

Of Hedges , or Inclosures.

1. AS there is no Countrey can have more need of planting
than this , so non more needfull of Inclosing : for we well
know how vain it is to plant unless we Inclose.

I spoke of Brick and Stone Walls, in Part 1. Chap. 5. Sect. 5.
Now for Hedges I preferre the Holly and Hauthorn , raised from the
seed, albeit there be several others. mix not Hedges , because
                                                        strong-

strong-growers over-growes the weak, neither suffer Briers, Bram-
bles, Docks, or Thissels therein.

2. Your *hollies* having stood two years in the seminary and two
in the nurserie, remove them by a trowall or a spade with a clod of
Earth at their Roots, croping such Roots as appears Without the
clod with a sharp Knife, and lessen its head by croping the side-
boughes, (cut not its top) plant in made up bordures, or at the back
of Ditches at a foot distance in good earth.   Let them stand two
years untouched except weeded, then cut their tops at a bud to
make them furnish thick, and ply their side boughes to grow
through other, like slicing or feathering, and next year fall to work
with the Sheers, cutting both sides and top as we use to do with
Box, &c. Never supporting or binding any Hedg, as is the Custome
of some: plant your *hollies* in *Aprile*, and when ready for sheers, cut
in *May* and *July* therewith, and so train them close from the bottom, but neither too broad nor too high.

3. The *hawthorn* having stood 2 or 3 years in the seminary, pull
them up and cut the ends of their Roots, and their tops within 4
Inches of the Root, and plant them within the fence or back of the
ditches in the good earth, delve them in spading by spading all a-
longst two rowes, a foot distance, standing in equilateral Triangles,
still thickning your bordure by adding good Earth *&c.*   Let them
stand 3 years untouched, except weeding and reparing where any
is dead; then fill them within half a foot of the ground, so will
they shoot furth a thicket of young shoots, which next year may
be train'd with the sheers, as before is instructed.

4. If you would Plant your hedge on the face of a ditch, as in wet
and tough grounds, then streatch a line at both sides of the intended
ditch, and ritt with the spade alongst by the same, slanting inward: for if the ditch be 7 quarters wide, it must be 5 deep,
(sloping to a foot in breadth at the bottom) then cut the turf or surface of your ditch, and lay a gang or row of the first spading a-
longst by the brink of the ditch (sloping at the face according to the
slop determin'd, with half a foot of table intercepting, because so
                                                            much

much will crumble doun by the frosts, &c.) On the top of that, lay one row of quicks, their tops standing up a little towards the ditch, cover their Roots with fine small earth, and lay another spading above them, and if you will lay another row of quicks above that, every one here opposing the mid-intervall of the other, and so cover on the rest of the mould till the ditch be finished: being all-wayes sure to put good earth next the quicks, thô you should bring it from some high-way or ridg of land next thereunto, and every year scour the ditches, claping it up about the quicks. or a farr better way is,

To cast half of the Earth that comes out of the ditches, to each hand, and quicks in both sides; accordingly this will make an Invincible fence: for then the hedg growes up on both sides of the ditch, the gutter betwixt makes it terrible. but that I am against the common double, (which is 2 ditches near other, and the Earth that comes out of both laid betwixt them, with a row of quicks in the face of each ditch,) is becauſe here the quicks are obnoxious to the croping of cattle; (besides they take much ground and the quicks are too much burthened with Earth,) rather if you be for such, make a little space betwixt of plain ground, where you may plant the Hedg.

5. But if you would have a row of Trees round by your ditches, then make these two ditches the breadth of a walk sundrie, but parallel, and in that mid intervall plant one single row of Trees, and the two hedges at the Back of the ditches: here you have two excellent walks of shade, nor is the ground lost between thir hedges; you may have good Hay, and in large quantity. And in effect this is the best way that ever I thought upon, for Inclosing and sheltering our grounds and plantations; and you may make the Intervall betwixt these hedges wider, so as you may have two rowes of Trees.

6. Now for fencing the quicks in all the several sorts from the croping of beast, as indispensibly necessary while young.

N   If

If the Hedg be planted alonght by the back or infide of the Ditch, then the ftreng Ditch with its Earth caften to both fides will fence it: and if you think that not fufficient, fet, ftake, and raife Hedg on the top of the bank, or rather (which is indeed much better,) cuttings of Thorns fet there in a fpade bit trench well backed: or for want of thefe, back up the Ditch with Turf, which is like half Ditching. But all this time there is but one fide of them fenced, and that next the pafture; therefore no beafts can come on the other fide to eat the Fogage, except teathered horfes: but if you make the hedg or Hedges and Trees betwixt the two Ditches (you may caft half of their Earth to each hand, and back them as is Said, which fences from all hands moft elegantly. And if you plant your Hedges in the face of the Ditches, the fame backing on each hand will alfo fence them.

But where you plant Trees at a great diftance through your fields or parks; you may fence every particular Tree by cutting a little trench round 4 foot off the Tree, and about 2 foot wide, facing it handfomly up like a ditch, laying one row of Turfs or fpadings above other, till it be 3 foot high from the furface, backing them with the fmall Earth or fhovellings, battering inward to the Tree; here the Tree muft be high planted: tho more the Soyl inclyn to wet, or the fourer that be, plant fo much the higher above the furface; you may ftick fome Briers, or Thorns on the top of this Tump.

CHAP. V.

How to propagate, and order Fruit-trees.

1. THE only Fruits for this Countrey are Aples, Pears, Cherries, Plumes, (and Apricocks, and peaches at Southside of walls,) Currans, Goosberries, Rasberries, &c.

Before I begin, I shall premise some observations on Graffing, &c. a sure means to obtain Fruits of the desired species, and that in short time: for by taking the twig or bud of such a sort as is a good fruit, and bears well, and Graff or Inoculate into a proper stock, you ar sure to have the same fruit; because the Graff dominires, albeit it may have a little smack of its stock whereon now Graffed. And you may expect fruit, because it may actually have the fruit buds, as being taken from a bearing tree. But if you sow the seed, they will be long e're they come to bear, and at length perhaps bring no fine fruit, and for the seed of Graffed Trees, they will not bring the same fruit; Pears, and Aples will rather bring a Fruit of the nature of the stock, whereupon they have been graffed; and although you should take a Cyon of the same, and graff in its self, that will not alter the Fruit, nor better the Tree, except a little check its aspiring, which may as well be effected by pruning.

Wee can also be sure of the desired fruit, by cuttings, layings, and circumposition; but such are allwayes Dwarfish and short lived Trees, as wanting a main Root which all seedlings have. Hence ariseth one reason, why stocks should be raised from the seed. Suckers are not so clean and lustie; therefore not so able to nurse the graffs, and they are apt to send Suckers again. Only I look upon plum Suckers as very good, because when they Spring off a Root at a distance from the stem, they strick good Root of themselves, very much resembling seedlings. Moreover you may

Graff

graff on a Root or a stock Sprung off that Root as in Chap. 1. Sect. 4. & 8. which is near equal to a seedling.

The seed of crabs, or wild Aples, and pears, may be fit to make stocks of such Trees designed for the fields, or more Rugged grounds; but for a cultivated soil I would choice the seeds of finer fruits. And so the great White-plum is the best stocks for Apricocks, or for want thereof any other White-plum with great shoots, albeit it doth on any plum: but we reject it self for a stock, as being too spongie and not so durable. But Peaches and nectarins, takes only best upon Peach stocks, so cherries on geens, and Plumes upon plumes.

Goosberries, and currans, needs not graffing; they do well by Suckers, layers, and cuttings.

To make Dwarfe Aples, Graff or bud on the paradise or any that hath Burry-knots, Codlings, Redstracks, &c. Dwarfe Pears on the Quince: but no Pear holds well on it (that I have tryed,) save Red Pear Achans and longavil; but you may re-graff for varieties. And if you be very curious for these stocks (which I am not) you may cut them at the Spring, when ready for graffing, within 2 Inches of the ground, and at *August* come twelve moneths Inoculate in that young shoot, and perhaps they will prosper the better. but I think graffing in the Roots of Pears, will produce Dwarfs.

Dwarfe-cherries on the morella, or on the common Red cherrie. Or on that Red geen spoken of in Chap. 3. Sect. 2. which is more Dwarffish than the black.

2. The mellow, warme and light ground is for fruits; and allthough the best, warmest and lightest land, yields most excellent corn, yet the strong, stiff, cold, moist yields not so good fruits, plants, Grass, Hay, &c. Aples affect a pretty rich loamy soil, tho they will bear in clay mixt with lym, dung, and Turff.

Pears will prosper well enough where the soil is mixt with Gravel. But both Aples and Pears are better relished in warme grounds that are not over moist, than in cold and wet: yet there be some grounds hath sweet moisture, others soure; Which last is very bad,

and

and therefore muſt be helped by draining and application of proper Medicine, ſee Chap 2.

Cherries, Plumes, Apricocks, Peaches affect a light, ſharp ſoil throughly prepared and mixed with Rotted manures. As to their propagation,

By Graffing are Aples, Pears, Cherries, Plumes, Quince, Medlar, Wallnut, Cheſnut, Filbeard, Service, &c.

By Inoculation or budding ar Apricocks, Peaches, Nectarines, Almond, Goosberries, Currans, Aples, Pears, Plumes, Wallnuts, &c.

By Suckers, are Currans, Goosberries, Barrberries, Raſberries, Quince, Vine, Fig, Mulberrie; its the white that feeds the Silk-worme: But that's to little purpoſe here.

By layers and circumpoſition are all ſorts.

By cuttings are Currans, Goosberries, Vine, Quince, Aples, eſpecially theſe with Burrie-knots.

By Nuts and Stones are Wallnuts, Cheſnuts, Filbeards, Almond, Peach, Plum, Cherrie.

By Kirnells or ſeeds are Aples, Pears, Quince, Goosberries, Currans, Barberries, Vine, Mulberrie, &c.

I have told whereupon to Graff Aples, Pears, Cherries, Plumes, Apricocks, Peaches; and as for the Quince you may Graff it on it ſelf or on the Hawthorn, Almonds on it ſelf, Medlars on Pears, or on the Service, Filbeards on the Haſſell; Service, Wallnut, Cheſnut, Goosberrie, Curran, all on their own Kind.

3. In raiſing the ſtocks obſerve that,

Aple, and Pear ſeed, muſt be ſeparate from the Fleſhy ſubſtance and ſpread to dry a little eſpecially the Cyder-marie, leſt it heat; you may roll it in Sand to help the ſeparation : keep it in a couch of dry Sand till Winter paſs, then ſow them as ſoon as the troſts are over; they come up that ſeaſon.

For raiſing Cherries or Greens ſee Chap. 3. Sect. 2. Peach, Plum, and Almond-ſtones muſt be uſed in all caſes as Cherries, only you may break the Peach Stones.

Uſe

Use the Quince-seed as Aples. As for the rest, I have shewed 'how they are increased in the last Section, and how to performe the several wayes in Chap. 1.

But you must prepare a seminary and nurserie, as before for Forrest-trees, see Chap. 3. Sect. 1. sow every species by themselves, keep them clean of weeds, and the next or second year after the seeds rise, if they shoot lustily, (draw out the biggest first) transplant them into the nurserie in single rowes 2 foot intervall, and half a foot in the rowes, for conveniency in hawing, graffing, pruning, &c. and observe to prun Root and side-branches in planting, as I directed with Forrest-trees; only when you have got them to a convenient hight for graffing, you may cut their tops to make their bodies swell the sooner, albeit this be not permitted with Forrest-trees. However graff and inoculat, while the stocks are young, e're they be an Inch Diameter, and they will sooner heal the wound: let them have a years settlement in the nurserie before you graff; but you may inoculat that same insuing summer after planting, especially if they be very free and lustie. Next year after graffed, remove them to a wider distance, *viz.* 3 foot one way and a foot the other. Prun there Roots at every removal, and enter a pruning, that they may provide for a well shapen head, cut them near now while young, if you would have all their branches of an equal greatness, and of order proper, as anon I shall inform you.

In setting your stocks in the nurserie, I presume you will set every kind by themselves *i. e.* Pears with Pears, and Aples with Aples, &c. And when you graff or bud, write down in your nurserie-book their species as they stand, *viz.* begin at the end of such a nurserie, and say the first row is graffed, with such a sort and so furth : and if you have more than one in a row, then set in a stake betwixt each species, and so write thus, from such an end of such a row; to the first stake is so many of such a sort or species; thence to the second stake so many of another, &c.

4. When you transplant Fruit-Trees into orchards, do, as I directed with Forrest-trees in groves; plant not deep, neither
trench

trench too deep; but tempt the roots by baiting the surface with dungs to make them run ebb within the reach of the Sun and shoures. Therefore mix the Earth in the holes (which should be 6 or 8 foot diameter) with Rotted neats dung and Earth well turned, sweetned and Prepared as in Chap. 2. Cover, delve, and haw their bulks as in Chap. 3. Sect. 3. and for further improving and keeping your Fruit-trees in good case, see Sect. 6. of this Chapter, prune their Roots at every removal, as Forrest-trees, (experience forbids me to make exception of the Peach or any other, as some doth) And proportion their heads to their Roots by pruning : but here note, that, as Forrest-trees are train'd up high bodies and unlopt heads, so Fruit-trees with low bodies, their heads lopt and branches topt; therefore easily proportion'd, as aforesaid.

Standards of 4 years old, may be planted out of nurseries into Orchards, Wall-trees of 2 years old.

The season of the year is as soon as they give over growing; (if the leaves be not off, cut them, saving a little tail of their stalks) its true you may plant any time in Winter, weather open, but rather let the frosts be over, and the spring Approaching, if you have missed the fore-end of Winter, which is the better season.

For standards are Aples, Pears, Cherries, Plumes, Goosberries, Currans, Barberries, Quince, Wallnut, Chesnut, Filbeards, Service: But I think all these deserves not a place in the orchard.

For Walls are Apricocks, Peaches, Nectarines, Almond, Vine, Fig, Currans, Aples, Pears, Cherries, Plumes, &c. But you need not take up much with Almond, Vine, Fig, nor Nectarine

On the south side of the Wall plant Apricocks, Peaches, Nectarines, Vine, &c. On the east and west sides Cherries, Plumes, Aples, Pears, &c. On the north side Plumes, some Pears, as great Bargamot, some Aples, Currans especially, and Rasps, &c.

When you elect them in the nurserie, hang sticks tyed at them
figured,

figured, and write the same figure on the Paper at their name to distinguish their species; and afterwards being planted write them, as they stand.

5. Begin betimes to prune your Fruit-trees, spare them not while young: reduce them into a good shape, and order while such; so will they not only Soon over-grow the wounds, their branches being but small, but also when they should come to bear fruit, you shall not need to cut so much, only purge them of superfluities; and this is the way to make Trees Fruitful as well as pleasant.

Some Ignorants are against pruning, suffering their Trees to run and Ramble to such a head of confusion, as neither bears well nor fair : for the Root is not able to maintain such, farr less fruit too; and therefore are their fruit so small and Imperfect; in the mean time the Tree spends its strength, and so cannot live long, nor make good service in their time: yea somtimes the Root is not so much as able to bear such monstrous heads; I know one windy day prostrate above half a score such in a little orchard.

Others again that are for pruning usually runs on the other extream, by cutting too much, and untimely ; and some sparing what they should cut, and cutting such as they ought to spare: but the general errour even amongst the learned is, that they spare them While they should prune, *viz:* the very first and second year in special, yea the first 5 or 6 years; and then they fall a massackering: at which time the branches being growen some of them greater than other, who now runs away with all the nourishment from the smaller; insomuch that no man can reduce them to order again, having thus neglected the time. Albeit you should endevour it by cutting deep, or exterminating these great branches, which I confess is the next remeed; but then as these wounds brings cankers, hollowness, &c. So doth the work retard their bearing fruit. And indeed its about the time that Trees ordinarly begin to bear fruit, that these unskilful

                                                                    men

men begin to prune: and the more they are thus cut in the head, the more they spring out to wood, and the less fruit they bear. But experience has taught me to begin, While young.

And when you do begin consider on the hight of the body, (for as high Trees are unprofitable, so too low Trees in orchards are inconvenient) for Aple and Pear standards two or three foot, plume and cherrie 3 or 4 foot, Dwarff and Wall-trees half a foot; there cut the top that Runs Straight upwards, making it to spread out in branches round. suffer no branch to aspire beyond other in hight, nor any to cross, Rub, or gall one another; and whatever branch or twig you cut off, cut close and clean by the body or branch (except in the case of old Trees and great branches as I observed in pruning Forrest-trees) and in toping of branches cut close and smooth Immediatly above a leaf bud, slanting upwards. And when you prun, spare the fruit buds (the full ones are them) except you see them too many; then purge by the Knife. likwayes if afterwards you find more fruit knotted than the Tree can be able to nurse to perfection, thin them in time.

But your first work is to proportion the head to the Root, by pruning; cut the tops at a convenient hight, that the Tree may grow equally furnished round; for cutting as it diminisheth, so it forms and shapes the head, insomuch as it furnisheth with new young shoots, that may be train'd, as you please.

Standards should have but four Arms breaking out for a head, opening equally round, these divided into branches, and again subdividing into twigs.& that you may the better understand what to cut, you may stand under, go about, look up through the tree where you may espy superfluities: keep them clear, void, open within like a bell and level on the the top. make some larger opens towards the the south for Sun-beams entrance ; let no branch grow cross through the heart nor shoot spring up therein ; (minding alwayes to prun such as cross, Rubs and galls other as above is noted)& any branches, shoots, or twigs that grows not the way you would have them cut them at the place whence you think they will send furth shoots

O

which.

which may lead the way you defire them: cut clofe, fmooth, and flanting at the back of a leaf bud tending that way; by this I bring Trees to order.

Wall-Trees efpecially fhould be cut near, while young, that they may fend furth a thicket of fmall fhoots for furnifhing your walls from the bottom, equally: and if you continue to top them every year at a convenient hight (perhaps about half a foot above the laft) that will make them fhoot all their branches of an equal uniformity of greatnefs, hight, and thicknefs, fo that no long, bair or naked branch be feen there, neither one or two great and all the reft ftarved fmall; the common fault of our wall Trees, and is occafioned through neglecting to cut while young even the firft year, as is faid above.

But albeit a Tree right begun and fo going on, yet one years neglect or wrong pruning may fpoil it: for as I was once pruning wall Trees, an Ingenious perfon ftanding by, faid I cut them too low, alleadging thereby, the wall fhould be long uncovered, defiring me to cut them a little higher: I told him, that was wrong, but for to fatisfie him I did cut 2 of them about 8 or 9 Inches higher than I defigned or fhould have don. The next year thefe two Trees left about a foot naked round, and above the fame crown'd like nefts while the reft was equally and orderly furnifhed; when he beheld this, his minde was changed, and I obleidged to cut exactly where I fhould have don the precedent year: which was now a little below the midle of the naked place, and this did put them feveral years behind the reft of bearing fruit.

You may nail them at midfummer that year of planting, and fo continue to do at the feafons herafter difcribed: prepare double plancher-nails and tags of hats, (which is better than leather) fhape the tags about half Inch broad, and betwixt 3, 4, and 5 Inches long, making a gafh with the Knife near the ends by folding, to put through the nail; then fpread the Tree, laying, plying, & nailing every individual branch by it felf, all at equal diftances from other, not clofe in one place and wide in another, and

and let non crofs other, the fuperfluous and thefe that will not ply eafily, and the exuberant or luftie that Robs the reft, muft be cut away.

Well plyed Trees will appear like apricocks; train, fpread, except thefe on a low wall, which you may caufe lean all one way, as half of the other: drive the nail but half way in, and on the upperfide of the branch, elfe it will lean and gall; at every nailing alter the old nails and beware of pinching tags, &c.

The time for pruning old planted and hardie Trees, is any time betwixt the leaf falling and the Spring, but let the frofts be over before you prune the new planted young and tender, and before the fap rife, otherwayes the frofts will penetrate the wounds and make a fore: but if you muft cut before the frofts, becaufe their heads may be obnoxious to the winds, (fuch are ordinarly the new planted ftandards) then yow may cut a little, and at Spring cut off thefe pieces left cleanly, as before is noted. Alfo let the frofts be over before you prune your Wall-trees and before they bud; only I ufe to let peaches bud furth a little e're I prune them, otherwayes pieces of their branches fomtimes perifh after the Knife.

And befides, that you muft Rub off all unneceffary buds, and pull up fuckers and weeds from the Roots, you muft alfo give all your Trees a midfummer pruning, (which is ordinarly the end of *June* & beginning of *July*) a good time to cut any fhoots of this year; any fhoots or buds as tend not only to the deforming your Trees, but Robs them of that fap, which may be otherwayes fpent in nurfing the Tree and its fruits, (but the fpring is the time of croping or cutting their tops untill the wall be covered, then crop at both feafons) thin & purge gently to let in the Sun, but not to fcorch the fruit. this is alfo the time of furnifhing your Trees with pedaftools or Bearers: therefore in repruning, fave as many of the likelyeft fhoots, as ar well placed, and cut them at the 3d or 4th bud from the Tree; but cut quit off the luftieft and greateft of this years (which Ignorants do fpare) & nail up fuch as are for filling up the defects of the wall.

You may go through them in harvest and purge the fruit of superfluous leaves which hinders the Sun: but do it so, as there may be leaves sufficient to screen the fruit, and cut quit off the lustie shoots of this second Spring, that Robbs the Tree and fruit.

As for goosberrie and curran standards, train them to a foot stem with a handsome round but thin head: these at Walls half a foot stem with a well spread head supported with Rodes layed cross, fastned with nails and tags. Rasps may be in shadowy bordures or beds a foot distance, kept clean of Suckers, weeds, and dead wood.

But because some years in some places we have ripe Grapes, especially that we have under the name of Frontinak: therefore if you think a Tree or two of them worth your while, plant them at a south Wall in a pure and fine mould, not wet, sour, and croud, but a light sweet soil mixt with some Cowes dung Rotted in heaps with the mould. Plant ebb and trench not deep; prune them every year, prune low in *February*, and at the true midsummer. Cut off the lustie young shoots and tendralls with sheers betwixt the 2d and 3d Joynt above the fruit; and in *August* purge it of superfluous leaves, but reserve so many as may screen the fruit a little.

There be some sorts of Fruit-Trees that will blow and bear themselves to death, when young or midle aged: For such cut most of the blowing buds, and thin the head to make it shoot again.

I got some cherries and other stone fruit from Holland, who tooke this decay: wherefore in the Spring I did cut off the blowing buds, and the branches near the place where the Tree headed, reserving only some buds for receiving the sap; (in case they should have put furth at the midle of the body or a little above ground) this made them shoot to wood. Therefore I conclude that by this and delving about, you may help ill-thriving Trees.

There be also some Aples and Pears, that will be full of false bearing buds, that doth not blow; such having got more head the

the Roots can well maintain, confequently has not ftrength fuf-ficient to fpare fap for bloffoms, farr lefs for fruit, which by pruning and thinning the head, and by flitting the bark of the body in the Spring, may be made afterwards to bear well, when they have put furth new fhoots at the head.

Some Trees there be that will not bear of themfelves till they be old: but if you cut off the head of the fhoots as foon as ever the Spring fhoot is over (which is at the true midfummer) and take out fome great boughs then, if you minde your time, and do it with difcretion, you may force that Tree to put furth blo-wing buds, and blow and bear the year following, as I fhall in-forme you in next fect: but,

6. One main bufinefs is to inclofe your plantations : avoid plan-ting too deep, too dry, too cold, too moift, and guard your Or-chards from winds by planting two rowes of Forreft-trees, at leaft round without the Wall, the breadth of a large walk therefrom with Thickets of the fame on the Weft, North and Eaft, but efpecially on the Weft. (Yet mind regularity) alfo obferve my methode of planting, and pruning and ordering their bulks of 6 or 8 foot Dia-meter : but when the Tree growes old and their feeding Roots farr abroad, you cannot reach to feed them with dungs in this narrow Compafs; therefore enlarg it, or otherwayes confine them a little fooner and hinder their too farr gauding, by digging a Circle round the Tree perhaps 8 foot Diameter, and cut all the Roots clean off there, that hath run out, applying frefh and fweet Mould, fo fhall they emitt Fibres or feeding Roots in thicket, which may be fup-plyed with refrefhments once in two or three years, as fhall be re-quired. And this cutting the Roots will caufe Trees, that are apt to fpend more in wood than Fruit, alter there-from, (add this to the latter-end of the laft Section) and the ends of the Roots cut off, and their buttends raifed up a little, will ferve as ftocks to Graff upon.

When you would enrich your worne out plantations, if the gro-und be poor and dry, add well rotten dung prepared and mixt with foil. The Water that foaks from a Dung-hill is excellent : for it will

fol-

follow the Roots and Enrich the Trees. If the ground be cold and moift, add Pigeons dung or Afhes and foot; which is alfo excellent if it be leopared with unskilfull dunging, or by noyfome weeds that grows about fuch Roots, (where the owner is a fluggard) & hatches or nefts, moles, mice, toads, &c.

If you obferve the premifes, you may prevent their difeafes, fuch as illthriving, &c. But if you have, or do neglect, and the difeafes be come, as if Cankers or Galls be entered, cut them clean out, covering the wound with a Plaifter of Cowes dung and clay compound; if the bark be pilled by hares, conies or mice, apply a Plaifter of the fame; (but better prevent the laft three, by fwadling the Trees with Straw or Hay ropes, unloofed in fummer and renewed every Winter, if your fence cannot Guard them.) Illtaken off branches, broken or rotten branches muft be cut off clean and fmooth. If any Trees be bark-bound, (which is the mifery of many and efpecially Forreft-trees) flit them in the Spring through the bark on both fides with a fharp Knife from the head to the Root, and delve about them, otherwayes raife and plant ebber if too deep; which is the common caufe of this difeafe together with bad inclofure.

If Jaundife, cut off the difeafed wood; if mofs, fcrape or finge it off: but its vain to attempt the cure untill you firft remove the caufe; which you will find to proceed from fome malignity at the Roots, whither the difeafe be Bark-binding, Cankers, &c.

And this moft commonly by ill-planting. (and not inclofing) as among Clay, Water, impenitrable Gravel, &c. Water muft be draineds, it an intollerable evil. Cold clayes, ftiff and hard foil muft be trenched and mixed with dungs and foils, often ftirred and fallowed, as above is directed. And if you would have Trees to profper, obferve their nature, and wherein they moft delight; and fo apply and help them accordingly.

9. And for deftroying of vermine, there is traps for Moles of feveral forms, befides you may watch and delve them up with the fpade. And for mice, the traps from *Holland*, or for want thereof, Pots funk in the Earth (where they haunt) till their mouth be level

with

with the surface half full of Water covered with a little chaff wherein they drown themselves; and so doth Toads, Asps, &c. Cast away the Earth where the ants lodge, supplying its place with stiff clay. Place Cow-hooves for the woodlice, and erwigs to lodg in all night, and so scald them early morning. Pour scalding Water in the nests of Wasps, and hang Glasses of Ail mingled with Hony, where you would not have them frequent.

Dash Water on the Trees for Caterpillers, by the Stroups we get from *Holland*. Gather Snails and Wormes, shoot Crows, Pyes, Jayes, and spread Nets before your Wall-Fruit for their preservation.

See the Appendix how to gather and preserve Fruit, and how to make Cyder, &c.

CHAP. VI.

Of Fruits, Herbes, and Roots for the Kitchen.

1. ALL the Fruits whereof I spoke in the last Chapter, are for the Kitchen or Table, but they grow on Trees or Shrubs; yet there is some falls in here, the tenderest whereof are

Melons, and are not worth the while : for you must raise them on the early Hot-bed (the making whereof is in Chap. 2. Sect. 7.) which (when fit for seed) prick 4 or 5 in together, at 3 Inches distance, through the bed, setting drinking Glasses on them at first, and cover on the matts over the whole carefully, to preserve from Snow, Rains, and Winds; taking off the matts in temperate dayes, but keep on the Glasses, except in a warme space; that you acquaint them a little with the Air, by raising the edg of the Glasses, with a little Straw on the laun side, closing it at night again. When they stand in need, Water with Water made warme by standing an

day

day or two in the Sun, impregnate with pigeons dung, but let it be fresh and clean, conveying it to the Roots, not touching their leaves with it : if they be sowen on the laft difcribed horbed *viz.* in cafes, fow at a wider diftance, and you need not tranfplant, but renew the heat when needful, and as they grow larger, cover with the Bell-Glaffes, giving them Air by hoifing the Glaffes, till they can endure the Sun without them, but ftill cover all clofe at night again : when they have put out runners 4 or 5 Inches long, cut off one or two joynts at the end, and when they have gathered more ftrength, cut off all but the prime fhoots. And when the Fruit knots, nip off that runner above the Fruit between the 2d and 3d joynt, cutting ftill off the new ones that fpring, but do not expofe the Fruit to the Sun: lay tile under the Fruit: wipe the Dew off the Glaffes and plants every morning, but keep the Glaffes on the Fruit, and Water non now.

Cucumbers may be ordered that fame very way, and fo may Pompions, but they are not fo tender, I have raifed them without Glaffes.

Strawberries are a very fine and delicat Fruit, and are eafily increafed, but beft by the fmall Plants at the ftrings when taken Root at the joynts: plant them at any or both fprings, but I find moft of fibrous Rooted plants apt to be fpued out of ground by Winter, if not Rooted fufficiently before. Dung, delve, mix and prepare a light and warme foil, prun their Root and top, and plant in ftreight lines 5 rowes in the bed, and fuffer them never to over-run, but keep each ftock by themfelves, ftill taking off all their ftrings, (except at fometime you permit a few for increafs) weed and haw among them; and in *September* cut them within 2 Inches of the ground, and lay Cow dung over the bed (referving their tops free) covered with a ftrinkling of Sand; this will much improve them. So as they will not need renewing for 6 or 7 years.

Artichoks is a fine and laiting Fruit, and is increafed by offfets chiefly, planted in the fpring, a fat and well cultured foil, light and warme, enriched with Sheeps dung, plant in ftraight lines, about 3 foot diftance having prun'd their Roots, and cut their tops within
half

half a foot; Water (if needfull) with qualified Water, and still cut away their under and hanging leaves, and haw the weeds as they begin to peep : when their Fruit is spent, cut them within half a foot of the ground, and delve and cover the plot over with dung and leitter, keeping their tops free. and in *Aprile* delve down the same, and extirpate them of Suckers, sliping them off carefully leaving 2 or 3 at most to each stock for bearing; And they will flourish near 9 or 10 years.

Great beans must be planted early in the Spring, as soon as the great frosts or over, in deep rich ground, 2 foot Intervall and half a foot in their rows ; these for seed when full ripe, cut and bind in little sheaves and lay on Trees to dry

Kidnes in *Aprile*, a light and warme soil, support them with sticks.

Peas that you would have early, sow in the full moon of *Novem*: if a warme place : but do not trust too much unto them. Sow in *Feb.* and hence monthly till *Iune*, that you may have them till the frosts surprize: in an open light, warme, dry soil ; and if they ly on the bair ground, they will sooner ripe by reflection. but if you would have them fruitful, set sticks amongst them while young, for their tenderals to climb on ; and keep them allwayes clean of weeds : when ripe, you may easily win some for seed, and sow not every year on the same plot; to change the ground Improves them. I preferre the setting them by lines, 5 rowes in the bed, as part 1 Chap: 5. Sect: 2. make the holes nimbly by the lines with a dible $1\frac{1}{2}$ Inch deep, and 2 Inches distance from another, or the same hand, fallowing, and put one in each hole ; then give the bed a smooth with the rake head, which fills the holes and covers the peas: one pound makes more service thus, than 3 otherwayes ; its soon performed, and they spring orderly.

2. Of Sallads and pot-herbes, the choicest sallad is Asparagus : sow its seed in *March*, good ground, and that time twelv moneths transplant into an exceeding rich and well mixed ground of Rotted dung and light Earth. you may streatch lines alongst

P   and

and crofs the beds and mark with the edg of the rule; then gather little huts of Earth at the croffings, whereon you muft fpread
the Roots of your Afparagus, two or three on a hut, but do not
top their Roots, (you may perceive their poynts are like the
runners of liquorifh) then cover the fets with the Rotted dung
and Earth, 2 Inches over, which has been lying a year in com-
pofe. They cannot abide wet grounds, and weeds will quyt deftroy them: at the Approach of winter, cut their ftalks, and
cover their beds with leitter and dung from the ftables. The
winter Raines will wafh in its fubftance to their Roots; at Spring
e're they peep, remove it, and loofen the Earth amongft them
with a fork, and cover them near half Inch with the mould Ra-
ked and evened; but do not tread on them. Follow this direction
yearly, and in 4 or 5 years it will be excellent for cutting:cut the biggeft and tendereft, and a little within the ground, but hurt not
them ready to peep; the feed is ripe when red.

You may have early *Afparagus*, if you plant fome ftrong
Roots on your early hotbed; which about a moneth hence will
Spring, and then dy.

Purflain may be fowen on the early hotbed, it cannot endure deep
Interring: fow on a fine mould like duft, and only clap it a little
with the fhovell; hence on the cold bed, but fat and fine foil
through the fummer, in drills for convenience of weeding and cutting: and if you pleafe tranfplant it when 2 Inches long, referve the early fowen for feed, till their pods grow blackifh; then
pull and hang to dry, and Rub out.

As purflain, fo lettice by feeds only, at the fame feafons;
(but the winter with corn fallad in *Auguft*) they love a fat foil
fomething moift, that for winter, more dry. Suffer thefe for
feed to run up, and only cleanfe of under and withered leaves:
It's ripe when it begins to fly with the wind; pull it, and lay on
a clothe, to perfect; and Rub out in a dry day.

Sow creffes at the fame times. And plant
Tarragon by off-fets in the Spring.

The

The small cherault by seed, as cresses. As also

Burnet: but it continues many years, still yielding seed.

Sampier growes at seaside in *Gallaway*, not so well in our gardens.

Succory and Endive by seeds and offsets at both springs; they continue many years.

Sorrall by offsets (some by seeds also) in beginning of *Aprile*, a good fat soil, a little shade, 6 or 7 rowes in the bed, weeded all summer, and cut near the ground in *Septemb*: In 2 or 3 years replant into another place: for they soon Impair the ground of that part appropriate for them.

Spinage by seed only in *Feb*: and *March*, but that sowen beginning *August* is most profitable; cut it beginning *Oct*: and it will Spring afresh. And be ready for Spring stoves; then reserve some uncut for seed; it prospers well in a very fat Earth, Not too dry.

And so doth beets, who are also propagate the same way, only them sowen at Spring are most serviceable.

Sow beet card in the fattest, and when something strong, you may transplant: they seed the next, not that year wherein you sow them.

Order burrage as spinage, its also Annuall; So buglos: but it continues many years.

Marigold may be ordered as burrage, and white Arage as Spinage.

Parsly by seeds in *Feb*: and *March*, they bring furth their seeds next year, whereby they must be yearly renewed.

Sellery in a light fat soil, 8 rowes in the bed, as parsly; it continues long, yearly yielding seed after the first; & so doth smalladg & Alexander. They may be blanched as succory and Endive, *viz.* sellery sowen at spring Transplante at midsummer in a very fat and fine earth, half foot deep furrowes, 3 foot between the rowes, and but 3 Inches in the rowes, and as it growes up, gather the earth at its sides from the Intervalls, leaving the top free; and still as it growes, earth it up; so shall it be blanched for a winter sallad.

Garleeks

Garleeks and fhallot by offfets in *March*, a light and fat foil, 8 rowes in the bed: I ufe neither cutting nor twifting their ftakes, but when their fibres begin to Rott latter end *Auguft*, take them up, and fpread to dry a little, and houfe them in a dry room with board floor for ufe.

Leeks by feed in *April*, a fat foil, though fomething ftiff, In *June* you may thin them by Tranfplantation : prun their Roots and tops, fet them at three Inches diftance, and continue to crop them till *Octob:* the french feed is beft, ours not worth the while.

Onyons by feeds in *March*, a Rich, Warme, light mould, well mixt with Rotted compoft, and fifted pigeons dung ; give them a thin coat or covering of earth. Sow alfo beginning *July* for *Shibols*; its not worth the pains to win their feed.

Plant offfets of fives in fpring, 9 rowes in the bed, in a rich and low ground.

Cole Flower is a fine cole; fow on the early hot bed, (for its hard to get winter plants through to purpofe) fow thin and ebb, and carefully preferve them from colds while young. If you water, Imbibe pigeons dung, but touch not their leaves therewith ; when their leaves ar 3 Inches broad, Tranfplant them into a very fat and well mixt foil, 2 foot diftance, prun their Roots and tops : and if any worm knots, cut them away, and in fetting keep their hearts Immediatly above ground. And all along keep them clean of weeds, under hanging and withered leaves: let them not fuffer drought while young, make the water like wort by dung. if the ground and feed be good, you may expect good heads ; which if you fpend not alltogether before frofts, (which fpoils them) take them up in a dry day and ty them in pairs to hang in a dry Room for ufe. the beft feed comes from *Candia.*

There be many Cabbages; fow the *Savoy* and fuch tender forts, as cole-flowers, albeit not fo tender ; fow the great white and Red, the full moon in *July*, Plant them furth in *Octob:* 3 foot diftance in well dunged ground : fet fome alfo in *March*; but then the gardner finds multiplicity of bufinefs, therefore its his wifdom to put as
much

much work by hand as can fuffer it, at leaft to have all his grounds
fallowed before winter. you may take up and hang your Cabbages in
Novem: as cole-flowers: but plant fome of the beft and hardeft for
feed, up to the neck; when they fhoot, fupport with ftakes and
Ropes; when full, cut and lay on a clothe to perfect. But choice
the midle, rejecting the lower branches.

Catch fnails and worms that graws the young fprouting plants;
and fet nets for birds at the fame time. the reafon why old *Cole* is
full of green worms is, dry poor ground never weeded, or otherwayes unqualified dungs and unfeafonably applyed. If they would
trench, mix, &c. As in Chap: 2. that their ground may be clean
and fweet, they fhall ripen accordingly.

Common Colworts ar ufually fowen at fpring, planted in fummer and eaten through winter, and at fpring when other green
herbes ar fcarce you may alfo fow and fet them with Cabbages and
ripe their feeds accordingly.

3. Of fweet herbes: as,

Clary by feeds and offfets in *Aprile*; at which time you may
flip and fet Tanfie, Sage, Coft, Mint, Balme, Winter Savory, Thyme, Penniroyall, Wild Marjorum, Maudlin, Fennell, &c. Prune their tops and fibres, and plant in a garden foil,
8 rowes in the bed; they all continue long: but cutting their tops in
growing time makes them more durable: and cut them all within
a handful of the ground at *Auguft*, that they may recover againft
winter. You may likewayes fow the feed of Fennell, Thyme,
Winter as well as Summer Savory, Dill, Sweet Bafill, &c. In
Aprile, a warme cultured foil, ordering them as above: the three
laft ar annualls. If you would have fweet Marjorum early, raife
it on the hot bed, the fweet Bafill requires the fame: fow it alfo the
latter end of *Aprile* in a warme fat foil, 8 rowes in the bed. you may
fow it in *July*, and Tranfplant when two Inches high, in a warme
bordure at a fouth wall; its feed with Bafill comes from hotter
Countries. Sow Rofmary feed in *Aprile*, or at the fame time take
its flips or cuttings and twift them a little at the ends, and dible in

good foil, on a fouth wall-bordure: but cut not their tops, they eafily root being watered in drought with foap water; you may ply it to the wall as Shrubs.

4. I am now come to Roots, they require a light Earth, deep trenched, fat fand mixt with Sheeps dung; its convenient that it be dunged a year before, becaufe new dung maks them forke.

Plant Liquorifh offfets and Runners in *February*, in this foil well ftirred and mixt, after which do not tread fave in the furrows, fix rowes in the bed, and cover all the Intervalls with leitter topt with fand, but let the plants be free: for this is to keep out drought the firft fummer; keep them allwayes clean of weeds and cut their ftalks near winter. let it ftand 3 fummers in the ground, and in *Novem:* take it up thus: begin at one fide of the plot, and make a trench, the whole deepth of their Roots, taking it out carefully (not breaking it) at the face of the fame, cafting the Earth ftill behind as you proceed; then cut off the plants, to divide carefully and lay them amongft moift fand in a cellar till fetting time. And becaufe it ftands three feafons you may have three feveral plantations; fo fhall you have it to take up yearly, if you plant accordingly.

Scorzonera by feeds and by offfets: (that is by parting the tops of the Root) fow in the Spring, or when its feed ripes promifcuouly in the beds; it continues many years in the ground, and growes ftill the greater, and is in feafon at all times for eating, tho it yearly run to feed.

Order Carvy as fcorzonera; its Roots is eaten as parfneeps.

Skirrets by feeds, but chiefly by offfets, plant the fmall fets not many in a bundle, in *March*, 8 rowes in the bed: when their ftalks begin to wither, fall a fpending them, and as you break off their Roots for ufe, lay their tops or fets in ground covered a little till the Spring for planting; (I cautioned you before to change the crops) thefe you fpend not e're the frofts come, hard houfe among very dry fand, that you may have them

when

when you will, rather as be barred from them by the frosts.

Parſneeps by ſeed only: ſow in *March* promiſcuouſly over the bed, but thin; ſpend and houſe them with ſkirrets, and cut quit off their tops, leſt they grow amongſt the ſand: reſerve ſome of the beſt untaken up for ſeed, which will ripe the next ſeaſon, choice the midle ſtem ſeed.

Beat-Rave may be ordered in all caſes as parſneeps, ſave that you may begin ſooner to eat them (*viz*: as ſoon as they are bigg enough) tho they laſt as long, beſides theſe you pickle.

Carrots as beat Raves.

Turneeps by ſeeds in *Aprile*, *May*, *June*, *July*, (the firſt proves not beſt) promiſcuouſly over the bed, very thin and ſcarcely any covering of Earth. When they riſe, thin them; late turneeps may be houſed as parſneeps and ſeeds reapt accordingly.

Horſe Radiſh by offſets, and laſts long too.

The Garden Radiſh by ſeed only: you may raiſe for early in the hotbed caſes; hence every 20 dayes with other ſallading through ſummer, beeauſe they quickly ſhoot for ſeed: ſow black Radiſh in *Auguſt* and *Septemb*: for winter, theſe ſeeds next ſeaſon.

Potatoes being cut in as many pieces as you pleaſe providing there be an eye at each piece and planted in *March*, 5 rowes in the bed, plant not deep, neither in wet or ſtiff ground; ſpend them with parſneeps, and in houſing ſpread only through a board-floor.

Parſly is alſo a Root for the Kitchen, and ſo is fennell; I ſpoke of them before, only you may houſe ſome for winter.

See part 1. Chap: 5. for the orderly planting of Kitchen herbes.

5. Weeding (I think) may be accompted the moſt material part of Gard'nery: The learned *Evelin* takes notice of it; his directions are, weed and haw betimes, continue weeding before they run to ſeed, which is of extraordinary Importance both

for

for faving of charge, Improvement of fruit, and the neat main-
taining of the gardens: wherefore fayes he, keep your weeds
doun, that they grow not to feed, and begin your work of hawing as foon as they begin allmoft to peep; by this means you
will difpatch more in a few houres than afterwards in a whole
day; whereas if you neglect it till they are ready to feed, you
do but ftir and repair the Earth for a more numerous crop, and your
ground fhall never be cleared.

And this agrees with what I had writen my felf, viz: deftroy
weeds while young: for when they have growen ftrong and got
deep Rooting, they'le not only take the nurifhment from the
good plant, but there will be fuch difficulty in grubing them
out, that the good feed or plant is in danger of being deftroyed;
but if you fuffer them to bear and fow their feeds, then (befides
that they exhauft much more of the fubftance of the ground)
you fhall find the work Intollerable, for they'le poyfon the whole ground, infomuch that one years feeds will coft many years
weeding: and therefore prevent thefe things by keeping doun the
weeds; fo fhall your work become eafie and gardens handfome.

In beds where hawes cannot go, you muft weed with your
hands on both fides, fitting in the furrow on a ftraw cufhion, pull
up the Root cleanly, taking the help of the weeding Iron where
needful: but make ufe of the haw in all the Intervalls, drill-beds,
nurferies, furrowes, tables, or pathes, whereby one will cleanfe more than fome fix by weeding with their hands; and if dry
weather, they'le wither where they ly cut, otherwayes Rake
them in heaps and fpread again when Rotted, or carry them to
fome open trench or pit, and ftill be vifiting your plantations, that
as foon as you perceive a weed peep, you may chalk it.

CHAP. VII.

Of some Physick herbes, shrubs, and Flowers.

1. ALL the herbes in the laſt chapter are phyſical, and having ſpoken to them already, I have the leſs to do here; however there is more, as

Garden-Rue: I uſe to environe ſage beds with Rue; (the ſoil not moiſt, mixt with aſhes not cinders) you may box bordures with it as well as lavender, or hyſop; which laſt is alſo Increaſed by ſeed, and ſo is golden Rod, feverfew, verven, celandin; they laſt many years, and ſo doth

Wormwoods, comfry, Solomons ſeal, Catmint, Callamint, Elacampan, Maſterwort, wall pellitory, garden Germander, Beatony, Camomile, Swallowort, Suthernwood, Lovag, Dwarf-elder, harts-tongue, Maiden-hair, Aſrum, Dropwort, Birthwort, Horhund, Spignell, Agrimony, Briony, Bearsbreach, Sea-holly, Madder, Rhuebarb, Dogmercury; all which are eaſily Increaſed by offſets in the Spring, and requires to be cut a little above ground at the beginning of Autumne.

Angelica, Spurg, ſcurvy graſs, &c. Are Annualls, but yield ſeed the ſecond year from ſowing: you may ſow when ripe, or in the Spring; but if you prevent their ſeeding by cutting, they will laſt longer.

Bleſſed thiſſell, Thorn Aple, Tobaco, ſtinking Arag, oak of Jeruſalem, &c. Yielding ſeed and dying the firſt year; therefore ſow yearly in *Aprile.* The Virginia Tobaco requires the hotbed, the reſt a good fat, light ſoil, as doth Angelica: you muſt not burie ſtinking Arag deep, ſow it as purſlain.

There be many more, beſides multitudes in the fields, Woods, Glens, Meadowes, &c. Of good uſe, many whereof you may bring into the garden as I have done: I forbear, ſeeing the order is in part 1.

Q

Chap. 5. and the wayes of propagation in the firſt of this, and how
to order the ground in the ſecond. I do not approve of planting the
clod with them brought out of the fields, for it rotts and turns
ſour, and ſo kills the plant, (albeit you may keep the clod about it
till you come home but,) then part it off carefully, prun their fibres a little, make the holes with the Trowall, and plant in a Connatural Earth, to that of their wonted abode, well ſtirred and aired,
which is ane excellent mean that makes all plants proſper, and
therefore diligently to be obſerved.

2. Of Shrubs that loſe their leaves in Winter, the choiceſt
whereof are,

Roſes of many ſorts, they are increaſed by Suckers and layers.
the muſk may be buded on the Eglantin and ſet at a Wall; the double Yellow bears faireſt Flowers, if you bud the ſingle Yellow on a
Frankfort, and rebud the double Yellow thereon, (I have done it
immediatly on the ſingle) planted as a Standard, a little ſhaded in
Summer, and kept clean of Suckers and ſuperfluous buds; and
any that blow not freely may be ſlit at the 5 diviſions of the hoſe.

Prune your Roſes after the Flower is paſt, *viz.* before the full
Moon in *October*, cut behind a leaf-bud and cleanſe them of dead
wood, and if you deſire fair Flowers, ſuffer but one Stem on a
Root and keep it low, and every 5th year, cut them down to the
ground, renewing their earth with old Cow dung.

Jaſmines, Honiſuckles, Pipe-trees, &c. by ſuckers, layers
and cuttings. See Chap. 1.

Mezerion by ſeed, as Hawthorn; they ly as long.

Of Shrubs that be ever green there is Box, Savin, Arbor vitæ,
Tameriſk, Privite, &c. by ſuckers, layers, and cuttings in
Aprile; a ſhade and moiſt fat ſoil till Rooted.

The Cherrie-bay is an excellent Green, and not very Apt to
blaſt, there is alſo Lauruſtinus, Philyrea, Alaternus, (I love not
Pyracantha,) Juniper, (I care not for ever green Oak and Cypreſs)
all by ſeeds, which muſt be couched in Sand before Winter, and
ſowen in *Aprile*, to riſe that ſeaſon except the Juniper, which lyes till
the

the next : tranfplant the fecond year after they rife in *Aprile*, remove by a Trowal, with Earth at their Roots, toping fuch Roots as appears without the clod, and leffen the head by thinning it. See where I have fpoken of Holly, for the fame Rules may be obferved for thefe to be fpread on Walls, but fave the top of Standards : they do all well by fuckers and layers alfo, except Cyprefs and Juniper. Be carefull to defend your feedling Greens while young, from fpring blaftings ; yet do not choak them for want of good Air.

The Pin, Cyprefs, and ever-green Oak, (the laft in'fpecial) will fcarce endure a removal from feminary, therefore fow them in drills 2 foot intervall one way, and half a foot the other ; and the next year after they rife, make a fpade-bit trench between the rowes, and work in cautioufly, till you difcover the running down Root at one fide, which you muft top with the pruning Knife, and level in the Earth as it was, cut off fome fide-boughes and thin the head : let them remain two years ; then remove and plant them, as is inftructed.

Greens that are beft worthy our efteem, are *Scots* firr for Standard, Holly for Hedges, the Cherrie-bay for Walls, or barren creeping jvy, which will neither blaft nor feck fupporting.

There is Strawberrie-tree, and Tree night-fhade, who are tender. But

Indian and *Spanifh* Jafmines, Mirtles, Oleanders, and Orengtree yet tenderer, wherefore I am not very curious of them, yet there is feverals in this Countrey has them, and are at great pains in governing them, by fetting them in cafes, fmall ftones at the bottome, filled with Earth mentioned for fine plants Chap. 2. Sect. 6. at the feafon Chap. 1. Sect. 4. Houfing in Winter between latter-end *September* till beginning *May*, giving them frefh Earth as they retire, and expofe them *i.e.* takes out the upper exhaufted, ftirring that below with a Fork (not wounding the Roots) and puts in its place, fome rich and well confum'd foil, watering on all occafions with Water, wherein Neats dung is fteeped (not touching leaves or ftem therewith,) whereof they are fparing while remaining in the Houfe,

cxexcept after long frosts, in whose extremity is used a little Charcoal free of smoak sunk a little in the Floor, and in warme dayes free of frosts and fogs, aquainted with the Air, but shut close at night again: and when they may expose to the free Air, yet even then sets them a week in the shade, having first brussed them from dust, &c. For my part I rather be in the Woods, Parks, Orchards, Kitchen Garden or fields measuring, planting, and improving the ground to best advantage. However I will here take a little turne among the Flowers.

3. Of Fibrous Rooted Flowers.

July-flowers are the best, and are increased by offsets, layers, slips, and seeds. A light loamy Earth well mixt with rotted soil of Cowes and Sheep, a year before hand.

Albeit I have raised many double by seed of my own reaping; yet the surest way to preserve the best, is by laying, because seedlings are apt to dy after they have born a Flower: how to lay see Chap. 1. Sect. 6. Plant out your layers at spring, and give these in Potts fresh Earth as the Orenge-tree, and yearly cleanse the old Roots of withered, dead, and Rotten leaves, and leave not above 3 or 4 Spindles for Flower, (if choice) and nip off superfluous buds lest they blow and bear themselves to death: and if any brust slit, as I directed with double Yelow Rose. At midsummer shade from afternoons Sun a little these that blow, support them against winds, set hoofs amongst them for catching erwigs their enemies; Water well in drought, sparing their leaves, preserve the Choice from too much Raines by laying the Pots on their sides, strick off the Snow when it lyes too weightie on them, these you will not to bear seed, cut their stalks as soon as past the Flower.

Stock July-flowers by seeds or cuttings; the seed of single will produce double, but the more leaves the Mother hath, the doubler shall the product be; sow and plant with carnations or July-flowers, they affect a soil with them.

Prim-roses, Couslips, and bears-ears by offsets in the spring, to when the Flower is past, *(viz. July)* they affect a good natural
Earth

Earth well mixt with rotten Neats dung : the finer forts loves a
little fhade in fummer, if in Pots or cafes you may tranfport them
to fuch at pleafure.

Great varieties may be raifed from feed fowen in Pots, the foil
aforefaid mixt with willow Earth in *October*, take head of deep interring bairs ears, fow them as purflain : fet the Potts and cafes with
them at the Southfide of a Wall till *Aprile*, at which time they
fpring, and muft be now retired a little as is faid; tranfplant in *July* to Flower next fpring, and neglect not to Earth up fuch as are apt
to work out of ground namely bears ears.

There is many other as
Noble Liverwort, Spring Gentianella, Virgines-bours, &c.
and ar Increafed by offfets in the fpring or by feeds at the fame time.
As alfo Columbins, Holihocks, Cransbill, Campions, and
Conftantinople Flowers, Catch Flyes, Pinks and fweet Williams,
Throat Worts, and Bell Flowers, *&c.* Or Dafies, Violets,
Spidder Wort, double Marfh, Mary-gold, by offfets any time
when fpringing.

Of Bulbo and Tuberous Roots there is
Tulipas of great varieties, Increafes them by offfets when their
ftalkes withers, which is generally about *June*, *July*, *Auguft*; this
is alfo the feafon for other bulbo and tuberos Roots ; keep them in
a cool but dry place till *Sept*: or *Octob*: and then plant them in a
light fandy earth with fat foil an Inch below the bulb, fo that the
roots may reach it, remove every three years and oftener if they affect not the foil : they may be raifed from feed but its tedious.

Anemonies the fame very way as Tulips, except that they require
a rich earth mixt with Rotten dung fo that it be not Rank.

Apply this alfo to Rannuculafes of the fineft forts.

Cyclamin Roots may be carefully parted in *July* and fet in the foil
for Tulips.

Crocufes and Cholcicums as Tulips, but requires a mixt rich
light foil.   And fo with
Irife Bulbofes (but loves a dry bed) and Narciffufes, Ornithogu-
                              Q 3   lams,

Iams, Jacenths, Hesons, Aconits, Hellibors, &c.

Likewayes Iris Tuberosus, Crown Imperial, and Lilias of severall sorts, Pionies, Cynosorches, &c.

Indian Tuberose is tender. See Esq: *Evelin's* Kallendar.

There ar many Annualls may be sowen in pots, and plunged in hot bed, and some under glass covers especially them sowen in Autumne, fas

Amaranthus, Marvel of *Peru*, flos Africanus, Convolvulus, &c. In *Aprile* you may sow them on the cold bed, if good fat warme earth, together with double Marygold, Cyanus, Nigella, Delphinus, Anterhinum, double garden and Corne Popies, Fox Gloves, Flos Solis, Flos Adonis, &c.

But if you would be further satisfied in the varieties of plants, consult the Learned and most Ingenious Mr. *James Sutherlands* Catalogue Phisick Gardner at *Edinburgh*.

4 I spoke before of preserving plants by housing. There is some that cannot endure the house, who must be set at the South wall, the potts sunck three Inches below the surface, covered with glass, first clothing them with sweet and dry Moss : or in prepared boxed beds with folding Glass frames to lift up and down at pleasure; because in all seasonable warme blinks of the Sun & shoures they may be discovered of all that covers them, thus : Treat choice Ranunculas, Anemonies, Amaranthus, &c. Neglect not to repair their earth as (in sect: 2) the Oreng Tree.

Plants standing dry in Winter, earthed up, or the Earth made firme about them are good means of preservation. Neglect not to cleanse all your plants of under and withered leaves, superfluous offsets, &c. See Chap. 1. Sect. 10. and see Part 1. Chap. 6. Sect. 7. For the orderly planting of Flowers. And I hope the Reader will excuse for this brevity, seeing each Chapter herein would merit a Book, neither will leasure permit me at present.

A N

AN
APPENDIX

Shewing how to ufe the Fruits of the Garden.

1. 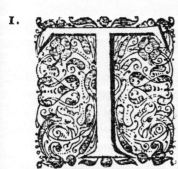HIS neceffarly depends upon the 5th and 6th Chapters, of Fruits and Herbes eatable.

Gather Aples and Pears when full ripe, efpecially thefe for keeping, or for Cyder in a dry day, clear but not froftie, in large Bafkets lin'd with Straw Matts, upon the 3 footed or ftanding leathers : at leaft lay Straw under, if you fhake them, and fuffer not too many at once thereon.

Gather Apricocks, Peaches, Plumes, Cherries, with your hands into clean Bafkets, when full ripe, whither for eating Green, preferving in Sugar, &c. drying, or for Vines; as alfo currans, Barberries, Rafberries, Goofberries. The Cucumbers for pickling muft be fmall *i. e.* e're their feeds grow firme; as Goosberries for baking, boyling, fauces.

Artichocks e're they grow too hard, let thefe for pickling be tendereft. Let the purflain for pickling be hard and old, lay it a day or two in the Sun to mortifie. That which you eat Green muft be tender. Eat Beans and Peas Green, but do not flice down the Beans, nor break the Peas ftalks, elfe them left thereon cannot fill. You may cut off the Beans with a Knife; and for the Peas, hold with the one hand and pull with the other.

Afparagus when tender *i. e.* about 3, 4, or 5 Inches high.

Lettice

Lettice when young, but its beft Cabbaged. Succory, Endive,
Sellery Blanched. Creffes, Parfly, Chervil, Burnet, when young
and tender. Sorrall, Spinag, beets before they fhoot for feed.
And fo is Arage, Marygold, Buglofs, Burrag. Shallot and
onions when their ftalks withered, tho fhibols are eaten green.
Leeks any time before they fhoot to feed. Coleflowers when
firme and white e're they fpoil; And fo cabbage when hard. Sweet
herbes any time either green or dryed, but gather them in their
prime for drying.

Liquorifh no difh but drink. fee Chap. 6. Sect. 4. where you
will alfo find feafon of Scorzonera, Beetrave, Carrot, Turneep,
Skirret, Parfneep, Potatoes, &c.

2. Befides what is faid above of planting and fowing at Spring,
fummer, and harveft for fomes longer continuance, as alfo of
raifing fome earlyer than naturally, by means of hotbeds, and
what I might fay of retarding others by tranfplantations, &c.
There be wayes of preferving them out of the garden, &c.

Aples and Pears may be carryed into the confervatory or fto-
rehoufe in the large baskets between two men ; which muft be
a clofe but cleanly and wholfome Room floored, lyned, and fi-
led with boards and fhelves of the fame round : let them fweat
a little on the floor with clean oat ftraw under them; then dry
and lay them Aple-thick on the fhelves, opening the north windows in fair, clear, windy dayes, efpecially at firft that it may
dry up the fuperfluous moifture. turne them fomtimes, and
in frofts cover them with matts, and fhut clofe the houfe: fome
of the choice you may wrap in dry papers fingly, and often vi-
fite, that you may remove any that begin to rott: for they quickly
affect the reft.

The way of preferving Cherries, Plumes, &c. In Wine, Cyder, Hony, or fugar is eafie, as alfo of drying them in the
oven.

And you may pickle barberries in Vinegar, and falt well dryed,
and fugar: to each pound and a half fruit, a pound of falt cold
again,

again, ¼ pound fugar beat to powder ; put them by layings in a well glazed Earth pot , and when they have ftood a whole week well ftopt powr in a mutchken Vinegar to each pound fruit; if you find the fawces too fharp put as much fugar as falt.

Range cucumbers the fame way, and ftrew falt, and Vinegar till they be all covered, and you may add a little dill and fweet bay leaves for odour, and cover them clofe 40 dayes unbroken: then pare when you ferve them up.

For Attichocks diffolve two large handfuls of great Salt (that is dryed on the fire in a pan) in one mutchken Vinegar and three of fair water, mix them while the Salt is yet hot, (but put not the liquor on the fire) boyl the Artichocks till the leaves come off eafily , and while the cleanfed ftools are yet warme, you may have 3 nutmegs, 3 drop cloves, 1½ dram mace, ¼ ounce white pepper, ½ ounce cinamon, beat to fine powder and ftrew upon them; then pack them in the pot with five or fix fpoonfuls the liquor on each ftratum: when all potted poure on the reft of the pickle, and ftop clofe.

To pickle them green put to every pound of cleanfed ftools an ounce Salt dryed and ¼ ounce fpices laft nam'd mixt in a mortar; and having dawbed the ftools full of holes, throw the powder thereon, when the pot is full, melt as much butter as cover them over two Inches, and when cold, cover clofe with leather.

To pickle Beet-raves, boyl and put them in glazed pots, with whole pepper and as much Vinegar as cover all over, ftoping them clofe.

Afparagus may be parboyled and pickled as Artichocks: and fo may green peas with cods.

Purflain as Cucumbers: and fo may taragon, fampeir, broom-buds, &c.

Lettice, Endive, Sellery, &c. By blanching and Ranging among fand in Cellers. Cabbage by Hanging. Roots by Houfing, Sanding, &c. As is fhewed in Chap: 6. Sect: 2. and 4. Sweet her-

R   bes

bes as well as physicall by Hanging to dry in some open Room not in the Sun as some advise.

Put marygold flowers in paper bags near the chimney till they pass hazard of mouldiness; do just so with true saffron. But because few knows how to order it, observe, to part its off-sets and plant with other bulbs at half foot distance in the beds or bordurs, it flowers in *Septem*: then be careful to go through in the mornings and gather the saffron *viz:* the thrums that are in the midle of the flowers, it bears not well till the 3d, 4th and 5th year; then you must remove it. But to the matter in hand.

3. As for the use of these fruits, the phisicians knowes their medicinalls, the cook their ordering in the Kitchen, the Gard'ner how to propagate and Improve them. For description and medicinal uses see our Countrey-man Doctor *Morisons* herbal; and for mechanicall uses, *Evlins* works.

To have dishes and drinks of them observe what followes.

4. Of dishes, as of Aples you may have baked without any ingredients save sugar, Rosted alone, and so boyled, fryed by shavers, with a little fresh butter, stew'd betwixt two plates, having cleaved and taken out their cors, add a little sweet butter and sugar. Of Pears you may have Rosted and boyled as Aples, also stoved being cut in fower and put dry in a stoup or oven of white Iron; and so set in the pot among water to boyl, you may have both Aples and Pears green with cheise.

Cherries are excellent baked, and so goosberries. Apricocks, Peaches, Plumes, Cherries, Currans, Goosberries, Rasber-ries are all excellent dishes green, or conserved. Strawberries and Red wine, or sweet cream.

Cucumbers pickled for sallad to rosted mutton: or if ripe, slice and lay them an hour in Salt, and so powr off their water. Ar-tichocks are either pickled or fresh, boyled and eaten with sweet beaten butter.

Beans and peas boyled with savory and thym fagot, served up with sweet butter beat amongst them, and set a little on a coal or chaffing.   Boyl

Boyl *Asparagus* in fair water, and ferve it up with a little fweet butter, beat *i. e.* tumbled in the Sawce-pan above the coal. The young fhoots of colworts will ferve the fame way.

Purflain may be eaten green with fugar and Vineger, or Oyl, ftew'd with meat, befides the pickled.

Lettice green as purflain; and fo creffes, Chervil, Burnet, burrage flowers, and wood forrall.

Spinag is excellent ftoves being boyled with lamb or Veall with a little forrall therein, as alfo choped difhes thereof with butter.

The fame way ufe beets; alfo make green broth of them with leeks, fagot of thyme and parfly. In fome ftoves and broths you may put Arag, Marigold leaves, Violet leaves, Straw-berrie leaves, Buglofs, Burrage, and Endive. In Pottage put Iuice of forrall, fagot of thime and parfly, and in moft of broths.

In the fawce or gravy of Roft mutton and capon and in all ftewed difhes bruife fhallot or Rub the difhes therewith.

You may ftove leeks with a cock. Onions may be baked with a little butter if you want meat: alfo make ufe of them with roft meat efpecially geefe, and to moft frefh fifhes in which parfly and thyme fagot is mainly ufed.

Boyl coleflowers in water mixt with a little milk; then pour it off and mix them in the ftew-pan with fweet butter feafoned with falt, and fo ferve them up about boyld mutton.

Boyl Cabbage with Beef, referving the top of the pot to powr on (when difhed up) about the beef.

Boyl Scorzonera, peale off its broun rind, wherein confifts its bitternefs, flice and fry it with butter.

When fkirrets ar boyld and pealed, Roll them in flowre, and fry with butter.

Boyl and peal parfneeps, chop and bruife them well, powre on butter, and fet them on a coal, and if you pleafe ftrew a little cinamon upon them.

Carrots are fo ufed or only difhed by fhavers. Beet rave boyld pealed, shaved, and when cold served up with vinegar and sugar: besides the pickled.

Beet-raves, Parsneeps, carrots are very good served up whole or sliced about meat, as turneeps usually with fat broth poured thereon.

Potatoes as Parsneeps: or for want of butter take sweet milk.

5. Of drinks, as of Aples to make cyder: I cannot name our cyder Aples, for I use to mix all the ripe at once in the orchard, that is of a fine Juice and easie to separat from the flesh, and pears that have plenty of Juice and hard flesh though harsh.

In France they extoll the Rennet cyder, in England the Hereford Redstrake. (Which in France they set at naught) they speak of genetmoil and musts, some pipens and parmains. And for Perry the bromsbury, and Ruddy horse pear. All which and many more *Hugh Wood* Gard'ner at Hamiltone has to sel. But now the different soils begets alterations in fruits besides the climate; yet both defects may be a little helped: The first by using all diligence to prepare the ground throughly, as is directed in Chap. 2. Fallowing is a most commendable essay.

The second by graffing and regraffing upon early: good fence and shelter round the ground are very conducible.

To make this excellent Wine, provide trough and beatters, press and harbag, lagallon and tappering fat, barrels and hogsheads; (for even by the common screw press I have made a hogshead cyder in a day) be sure your vessells be sweet, else you spoil all; white Wine, Sack-cask or such as keept cyder before. I have heard of cyder-cask 3 Inches thick in the staves, which I believe is of great Advantage in preserving the liquor: but if any be tainted, put a little unslaked Lyme Stone, and a little water in the Barrell, and stop it close; when stood a little while and jumbled, pour out and wash clean, that will cure.

The fruit being gathered ripe, as before, let them ly ten or twelve dayes, if summer fruit; and near the double of that time, if winter sorts: (but the late ripe that gets frosts is not good
                                                                        cyder)

cyder *)* mix not with unripe ones, neither suffer leaves nor stalks among them. When they are small beat, put them in the harbag within the press fat, and so screw them hard again and again ; and emptie it thereof and put in more, and do as before : and empty the receiver into the tappering fat, and therein cover it close with a canvass till the morrow at that time, before you tun it ; where the gross lee may fall to the bottom, then draw it off at a tap three Inches from the bottom, leaving that dreg behind. (The which may go among the pressings for water cyder) the clearer you tun it into the barrels, the less it ferments, and that's best cyder: for often cyder spends its strength to free it self of the grosser parts ; therefore while your cyder ferments, leave the vent pin loose, but keep close the bung for preserving the prodigall wast of its spirit ; and as soon as the working begin to allay, drive the vent pin dead to: and this will be perhaps in a fortnight, if it begins to work Immediatly, some times not till the Spring. But keep fast the pin till it begins to work, and that you mind to bottle of it, do as soon as fully clear and fine; which is ordinarly at Spring. Put a plum great of fine white loaf sugar in each bottle, and above all, make your corks fast and close ; then set them in the celler amongst sand.

To make the water cyder put $\frac{1}{2}$ as much water as you had cyder upon the new pressed marce, to stand covered in tubs 4 or 5 dayes: then press them and boyl the liquor, scumming it till the scum cease to rise fast, then take it off (for too much boyling wasteth its spitits) and put in tubs or coolers, and when cold tun it up ; when done working (which will not be so violent as best cyder) make the pin fast and in a short time, its for drinking. A little ginger, cloves, juniper berries or such may be boyl'd in it, if they please your tast.

The making of Perry differs not from that of cyder.

To make Cherrie Wine, to every pound ripe fruit stampt, put a Chopin Spring-water and $\frac{1}{4}$ pound fin white sugar, boyl the water and sugar, scum it and put in the juice of your Cherries, let it boyl up again, take it off the fire, run it through a hair-sive and when its throughly cold, put it in a stone pot, and after 6 or 7 dayes

draw

draw it into bottles, putting a bit loaf fugar in each; in a quarter year you may fall a drinking, it will keep a year; if you would have it ftronger, then ufe no more water than fugar.

After the fawe manner you may make wine of Rafps, Currans, Goosberries. or

Take currans very ripe, bruife and ftrain them, and to every pint of the Iuice put a pound and ¼ fugar into a ftone or earthen pot, fcum it often, and at a weeks end draw it off, and take out the fetlings and put in the liquor again; do this till it be fine, then bottle it; and at a weeks end if it be not fine in the bottles, fhift it into other bottles.

Gather your Goosberries e're they be too ripe, and for every three pound ftampt fruit, a chopin of water and a pound fugar: fteep them 24 houres, then ftrain them, put the liquor into a a veffell clofe ftopt a fortnight or three weeks, then draw it off if you find it fine, otherwayes fuffer it longer, and if not fine yet rak it.

Its ufuall to make it thus unboyl'd, becaufe it contracts a broun colour in boyling.

To every pint Rafps a pound fugar, let them ftand two dayes in an earthen pot, often ftirring and bruifing them; then put them in a woollen bag to hang up 24 houres and more till the liquor drop out into a ftone pot, fuffer it there till fermented and fcum'd, and at a weeks end (or fooner if fine) bottle it, and at another weeks end fhift it into frefh bottles, that you may leave the fetlings behind: thus fhift them fo long as you fee any fettlement, the which you may put in a bottle by it felf.

Of fome forts of Plumes, as damafons, &c. may be made wine.

That called Cherrie brandie, is a bottle half full of geens, fill'd up with brandie, fomtimes Jumbled a little; and in a moneths time is fit for drinking. Or if you put the like quantity of Goosberries inftead of Cherries; that will make the brandie very Delicious.

Cherries beft for wine are blackheart, morella. I think the
                                                                    red

red geen moſt excellent. See Chap. 3. Sect. 2.

-Of Gooſberries the great Chryſtal , and of currans the greaₜ Dutch red , alſo the red Raſp.

To have Ail of Liquoriſh, ſlice it very ſmall and pour Water on it when at the boyl : there cover it cloſe till the morrow , powr off this wort, and on more hot-water, to ſtand as long to ſearch it throughly , add your worts together and boyl with a little dry Wormwood *Carduus Benedictus*, but the greateſt difficulty is to barme it when cold , as wort of malt ; yet the ſtronger you make it , the eaſier it will take, or if you have the conveniency of ſettlings of good wort of malt to boyl with it ; that will facilitate the work.

ı To have good metheglin, take one part of clarified Hony and eight parts of pure Water and boyl well together in a Copper veſſel till the conſumption of the half : but while it boyls take off the ſcum , and when done boyling and beginnes to cool , tun it up , and it will work of it ſelf; as ſoon as done working, ſtop it very cloſe. Some adviſes to bury it under ground three moneths, and that to make it loſe both ſmell and taſt of Hony and Wax , and taſt very like Wine. I uſe to add dry Roſmary and ſweet Marjorum in boyling : ſome barms it as Ail ; which I have practiſed effectually.

6. To know what Fruits and Herbes to make choice of for our plantations :

The *French* Fruit ſucceeds not well with us, in *England* are good Aples, but *Holland* for Ston-fruit eſpecially Peaches and Cherries, and *Scotland* for Pears.

The beſt Aple for the Table is the Golden Pepin, we have alſo Rennets, Ruſſets, &c. very good. And for the Kitchen the Codling, Lidingtown, and Rubies, with hundreds for both.

But the beſt Pears for the Table are *Engliſh* Bergamot, Swanegg excellent Pears, and red Pear Achans, &c. The wardens are good Keepers and Kitchen Fruit, and multitudes more.

Of Cherries, the Kentiſh, and Morella, &c.

Of Plumes, Primordials, Muſſell, Imperial, &c.

The common and Orenge Apricoks , the newington and nut-

nutmeg Peaches, (Peaches bears better with us than Apricocks.)
The *Portugall* Quince, and thinshell'd Wa'lnut.

Of Goosberries great White, great Red, and great Yellow.

Of Currans the great red *Dutch*, early red, and the white.

Of Rasps, both the white and red.

The great red Straw-berrie, and the *Virginian* which is more early.

Of Artichocks both the great and the prickly.

Great white Beans, and white Kidnees. Of Peas Barnees, Hot-spures, Hasties, and the sickle Peas, &c.

If you can get Hordium nudum that is naked barley, and sow as I directed with Peas, it yealds an incredible increafs.

The *Dutch* Afparagus and Cabbage lettice. The forrall that ufu-ally fhoots not for Stoves, &c. And Yellow wood and *French* for Sallades. The white Beet and fmooth Spinage. Curled Parfly and Creffes. Shallot and Roccumbol, *French* leeks, and *Straws-brugh* onions.

Candy Cole-flower and our own great *Scots* white Cabbage.

Crifp Tanfie, and curled Spearmint. Sweet Fennell, and common Rofmary. Sweet Marjorum and red Sage.

The black Scorzonera and Orenge Carrot. The fmall round fmooth Turneep. Smooth *Dutch* Paifneep and fmall Radifh clear as Chryftall. See Chap. 6. for more.

Its to be noted, that the ingenious and moft induftrious, *Hugh Wood* Gard'ner at *Hamiltoun* can acommodate you with the above mentioned Fruits, together with multitudes of other forts, whither *Englifh*, *Dutch*, or *Scots*.

The

THE
CONCLUSION
Proposing SCOTLANDS Improvement.

THere is no way under the Sun so probable for improving our Land as Inclosing and Planting the same: Therefore I wish it were effectually put in practice.

FINIS.

Because of the Authors absence there are several things escaped the press: wherefore the Reader is earnestly desired to amend these here marked, viz.

Pag. 1. line 22. these garrets Read these, Garrets   Pag. 3. l. 20. Centre at least, the r. Centre, at least the   Ibid l. 31. confirments r. confinements   P. 9. l. 21. 90 degrees r. 60 degrees   P. 11. l. 30. fig. 2. r. of fig. 2.   P. 17. l. 17. Pole r. Pole so,   P. 27. l. 9. from by hawing. r. from weeds by hawing. Ibid l. 11. train r. trimm   P. 28. l. 25. side, each r. side of each   P. 32. l. 3. drawing r. draining. Ibid l. 18. recovering, r. recountring,   Ibid l. 24. conveniency; in viewing there r. conveniency in viewing; there   P. 33. l. 9. make r. marke   P. 35. l. 25. know reason r. know no reason   P. 36. l. 23. move r. more.   P. 41. in the example of division the figures above the dividend stands one place too farr towards the right hand P. 52. l. 26. 23. r. 32. P. 60. l. 10. Cirumposition r. Circumposition Ibid l. 31. sow r. saw P. 61. l. 32. by r. be   P. 70. l. 16. heatly r. heathy   P. 78. l. 3. seed in the wood, they r. seed, in the wood they   P. 84. l. 24. fill them r. fell them (i e. to cut off a Tree)   P. 89. l. 28. marie r. marce. P. 92. l. 17. know r. knew   The Page before 96. l. 4. apricocks; train, spread, r. a Peacocks train spread; Pag. 96. last line head the r. head than the   P. 101. l. 10. or r. ar   Ibid l. 26. distance from another. r. distance: another   Pag. 103. l. 1. cherault r. chervil   P. 105. l. 7. graws r. gnaws   Ibid l. 19 Balme. r. Bawme,   P. 108. l. 29. chalk r. check   P. 112. l. 33. ,0 r. or   P. 113. l. 29. Ranunculases r. Ranunculuses   P. 121. l. 21. r. one third   P. 122. l. 4. sawe r. same

THE
GARD'NERS KALENDAR

Shewing

The moſt ſeaſonable times for performing his

HORTULAN AFFAIRS,

Monthly throughout the Year:

AND

A Catalogue of ſuch diſhes and drinks as a compleat Garden can afford in their ſeaſons.

Publiſhed for the Climate of SCOTLAND
By JOHN REID Gard'ner.

EDINBURGH,
Printed by DAVID LINDSAY, at the foot of Heriot's-Bridge, 1683.

Reader,

As in this little Kalendar *thou will find when* ; *ſo in my Book* (*Intituled the* Scots-Gard'ner!) *thou will find how, to performe the particulars.*

The Gard'ners year is a circle as their labour, never at an end. Nevertheleſs their terme is

NOVEMBER.

COntrive or forecaſt where, and what you are to ſow and plant. Trench and fallow all your vacant grounds. Prepare and mix ſoils and compoſts throughly: miſs not high-way Earth, cleanſings of ſtreets; make compoſitions of dungs, ſoils, and lyme. Lay bair Roots of Trees that need, and dung ſuch as require it. Plant all fruit Trees, Forreſt-trees, and ſhrubs that loſe the leaf, alſo prune ſuch. Plant cabbage. Sow haſties for early peas in warme grounds but truſt not to them.

Gather the ſeeds of holly, yew, aſh, &c. Ordering them as in Chap: 3. furniſh your nurſeries with ſtocks.

Shelter tender evergreen ſeedlings. Houſe your Cabbag, Carrots, Turneeps: and any time e're hard froſts your Skirrets, Potatoes, Parſneeps, &c. Cover Aſparagus, Artichocks, as in the laſt moneth. Sow bairs-ears, plant Tulips, &c. Shut the conſervatory. Preſerve your Choiceſt Flowers. Sweep and cleanſe the walks of leaves, &c. Stop your bees cloſe ſo that you leave breathing vents.

Garden Diſhes and Drinks in Seaſon, are.

Cabbage, Coleflower, Onions, Leeks, Shallot, &c. Blanched Sellery, Succory, Pickled Aſparagus, Purſlain, &c. Freſh Parſneeps, Skirrets, Potatoes, Carrots, Turneeps, Beet-rave, Scorzonera, parſly and fennell Roots.

Aples, Pears, &c.

Cyder, Perry, wine of Cherries, Raſps, Currans, Goosberries, Liquoriſh, Hony, &c.

A 2

DECEM.

DECEMBr.

Rench and prepare grounds. Gather together composts. plant Trees in nuseries. and sow their seeds that can Endure it. Gather Firr seed, holly berries, &c. Take up liquorish. Continue your care in preserving choice Carnations, Ancmonies, and Ranunculuses from Raines and frosts. And keep the green-house close against the piercing colds. Turne and refresh your fruit in a clear and serene day. Sharpen and mend tools. Gather oziers and hassell Rods and make baskets in stormy weather. Cover your water pipes with leitter left the frosts do crak them, feed weak bees.

Garden Dishes and Drinks in season.

Colworts, Leeks, &c. Housed Cabbage, Onions, shallot. Several dryed sweet herbes. Housed Parsneeps, Turneeps, Skirrets, Carrots, Potatoes, Beat-rave, Scorzonera, parsly, Fennel Roots. Pickled Cucumbers, Barberries, Artichocks, Asparagus, Purslain, &c.
Housed Aples, Pears. Conserved Cherries, Plumes, Peaches, Apricocks, &c.
Wine of Aples, Pears, Cherries, Liquorish, Hony, &c.

JANUARY.

JANUARY.

PRepare the ground, foils and manures. Fell trees for mechanical ufes. Prune Firrs, plant Hawthorn Hedges, and all Trees
and Shrubs that lofe the leaf weather open. Alfo prune the more
hardy and old planted. Dung the Roots of Trees that need, draining exceffive moifture, gather Graffs e're they fprout, and near the
end Graff; begin with the Stone Fruits. Gather Holly-berries,
Firr hufks, &c. Secure choice plants as yet from cold and wet,
and earth up fuch as the frofts uncovered.
Feed weak bees, alfo you may remove them.

Garden Difhes and Drinks in feafon.

Coleworts, Leeks, &c. Dry fweet Herbes. Houfed Cabbage, Onions, Shallot, Parfneeps, Skirrets, Potatoes, Carrots, Turneeps, Beat-rave, Scorzonera, Parfly and Fennel
Roots in broth.
Pickled Artichocks, Beet-raves, &c. Houfed Aples, Pears,
and other conferved Fruits.
With Cyder and other Wines as before.

FEBRUARY.

Plant any Trees or Shrubs that lose the leaf, also lay and circumpose such for increafs, see *June*. Likewayes sow all your Seeds, Kyes, Kirnells, Nuts, Stones; also the feeds of several Greens, as Holly, Yew, Philyrea, Laurells, &c. Prune Firrs, &c.

Continue to deftroy Vermjne.

Graffing is now in feafon, fee the laft moneth.

Prune all Trees and Shrubs except tender Greens. Nail and drefs them at the wall. Cover the Roots of Trees layed bair the fore-end of Winter, if any be. Plant Hawthorn Hedges, Willows, &c.

Plant Liquorifh, Potatoes, Peas, Beans, Cabbage. Sow Parfly, Beets, Spinage, Marygold, and other hardy Pot-herbes.

Let carnations and fuch fheltered Flowers get Air in mild weather. But keep clofe the Green-houfe.

Now you may remove bees and feed weak ftocks.

Garden Difhes and drinks in feafon.

Cole, Leiks, fweet Herbes. Onions, Shallot, houfed Cabbage, Skirrets, Turneeps, Parfneeps, Potatoes, Beat-rave, Scorzonera, Carrots, befides Parfly and Fennell Roots.

Pickled Beat-rave, Artichock. Cucum: Houfed Aples, Pears, and other conferved Fruits with Cyder and other Wines and drinks, as above.

MARCH.

REdelve, mix, and Rake your ground for Immediat uſe. Delve about the Roots of all your Trees. Yet plant Trees and rather greens. Alſo prun ſuch except the Roſinious. Propagate by laying circumpoſition, and eſpecially by cuttings. Sow the ſeeds of moſt Trees and hardy greens. Cover theſe Trees whoſe Roots lay bair, and delve doun the dungs that lay about your young Trees all winter, covering on leitter again topt with Earth to prevent drought in ſummer: this is a material obſervation and more eſpecially for ſuch as are late planted. Slit the bark of ill thriving Trees. Fell ſuch as grow croked in the nurſerie. Graffing is yet in ſeaſon, (but too late for ſtone fruit) cut off the heads of them Inoculated.

Set peas, beans, Cabbage, Aſparagus, Liquoriſh. Sow parſly, beets, Endive, Succory, Bugloſs, Burrage, Sellery, Fennell, Marigold. Plant ſhollot, garleeks, Potatoes, Skirrets. Sow Onions, Lettice, Creſſes, Parſneep, Beet-rave, Radiſh, &c, And on the hotbed coleflour, and if you pleaſe cucumber, &c.

Slip and ſet phyſick herbes, *July*-flowers, and other fibrous Rooted flowers. Be carefull of the tender, the peircing colds are now on foot. Turne your fruit in the Room but open not yet the windows.

Catch Moles, Mice, Snails, Worms, deſtroy frogs ſpawn, &c.

Half open paſſages for bees, they begin to fit, keep them cloſe night and moring: yet you may remove them.

Garden Diſhes and Drinks in ſeaſon.

Both green and houſed herbes and Roots: alſo Pickled, Houſed, and conſerved fruits: with their wines as in the former months.

APRILE.

APRILE.

Plant Holly Hedges and Hawthorn too if not too foreward. Ply and sheer Hedges. Nail and prun Wall-trees, &c. Sow and plant firrs, and other greens. Slip and set sage, Rosemary, thym, Rue, Savory, and all fibrous Rooted herbes and Flowers. uncover and dress strawberries. Plant Artichocks, slip them and delve their plottes. Set Cabbage, Beans, Peas, Kidnees. sow Asparagus, Parsly, Beets, and Beet-card. Set Garleeks, Shallot, Potatoes, Skirrets, Sorral. sow Onions, Leeks, Lettice, Cresses, Radish, Orach, Scorzonera, Carvy. Fennel, &c. And on the hotbed Cucumbers, Coleflowers, Purslain, sweet Marjorum, Basill, Summer Savory, Tobaco, &c.

Set Strawberries, Violets, July-flowers, &c. Also sow the seeds of july flowers. &c. Sow all your Annuall flowers and Rare plants some requiring the hotbed. Destroy Moles, Mice Worms, Snails. Lay, Beat, and Roll gravel and grass. Fall to your mowing and weeding.

Open the Doors off your bee-hives now they hatch.

Garden Dishes and Drinks in season.

Onions, Leeks, Colworts, Beets, Parsly, and other herbes: Spinage, Sorral. Scorzonera, green Asparagus, Lettice and other Sallads. Pickled Artichocks, Beet-rave, Barberries, Cucumbers.

Housed Aples and Pears, Conserved Cherries, Plumes, Peaches, Apricocks, Goosberries, Currans. Also the wines of Aples, Pears, Cherries, Liquorish, Hony, &c.

MAY.

M A Y.

PUll up fuckers and haw about the Trees. Rub off unneceffary buds. Sheer or clip Hedges. Prun tender Greens, (Not the Rofinious) bring furth the houfed ones refrefhing & trimming them. Plant all forts of medicinal Herbes. Sow all fweet ones which are tender.

Gather Snails, Wormes, catch Moles.

Sow Letice, Creffes, Purflain, Turneep, Radifh, Peas, &c. Continue weeding and watering.

Near the end watch the Bees ready to fwarm.

Garden Difhes and drinks in feafon.

Coleworts and other Herbes, (being eaten with contentement is better than a fatted Ox without it) fage (with Butter,) Leeks, Parfly, Thyme, Marjorum, forrall, Spinage, &c. Scorzonera, Afparagus, Letice, Purflain, and other Sallades and Pot-herbes.

Pickled Artichocks, Barberries; Beet-rave, Cucumbers, houfed Aples and Pears for many ufes. Early Cherries, Straw-berries, near the end.

Cyder, Metheglin, Liquorifh Ail, &c.

B   JUNE.

J U N E.

CLeanfe about the Roots of Trees, Suckers and weeds, watter their Covered Bulks: efpecially the new planted.
Fell the long fmall ill-train'd Forreft-trees in the nurferie within halt foot of the ground. Unbind graffs. Prun all Wall and Standard Trees. Towards the end you may Inoculat. And increafe by circumpofition.

Gather Elm feed and fow Immediatly.

Tranfplant Coleflowers, Coleworts, Beets, Leeks, Purflain,&c. In moift weather; at leaft water firft the ground if dry.

Sow Peas, Radifh, Turneep, Letice, Chervil, Creffes, &c. Deftroy Snails, Worms, &c.

Begin to lay carnations or July-flowers: fhade, fupport and prun fuch as will blow. Water pots and thrifty plants. Weeding and mowing is in feafon, and fp is diftillation.

Bees now Swarm, look diligently, to them.

Garden Difhes and Drinks in feafon.

Cole, Beets, Parfly, Sorrall and other Pot-herbes. Purflain, Letice, and other Sallads: Radifh, Scorzonera, Afparagus. Green Peas and Artichocks. Green Goosberries. Ripe cherries, Rafps, Currans, Straw-berries.

Houfed Aples and Pears.

Cyder, Metheglin, &c.

JULY

J U L Y.

FAllow ground as foon as the crop comes off. Prune and purge all Standard-trees. Ply, Nail, Prune, and drefs your Wal-trees. Pull up fuckers and weeds. Haw and Water where need-ful. Inoculat Fruit-trees, Shrubs, rare Greens, Flower-trees; Increafe the fame by laying. Clip your Hedges after Rain. Suffer fuch Herbes and Flowers to run to feed as you would fave: Cut-ting the reft a handful from the ground.

Sow Turneep, Radifh, Lettice, Onion, Cole-flower, Cab-bage, and Coleworts in the full Moon. Near the end fow Beets, Spinage. &c. You may plant Strawberries, Violets, Camomile. Lay July flowers. Plant their feedlings. Slip and fet Hypaticas, Bears-ears, Couflips, Helibors, &c. Take up Bulbo and Tube-rous ones that are dry in their ftalks (if you mind to change their places) and keep till *September*, but fome would be fet imme-diatly.

Supply voids with potted Annualls. Lay Grafs and Gravell. Make Cherrie and Rasberrie Wine, &c.

Prevent the Bees latter fwarmes, Kill Drons, Wafps, &c.

Garden *Difhes and drinks in feafon.*

Beets and many Pot-herbes and Sweet-herbes.
Beet-card, Purflain, Lettice, Endive, &c.
Cabbage, Cole-flower, Scorzonera, Beetrave, Carrot, Ra-difh, Turneep, Peas, Beens, and Kidnees, Artichocks, Straw-berries, Rafps, Currans, Goosbeeries, Cherries, Plumes, fummer Pears and Aples, Cyder, Metheglin and other Wines.

AU

AUGUST.

FAllow bordures, Beds, Nurſeries, and the bulks of Trees. Yet Inoculat. Ply and purge Trees. Pull up ſuckers and weeds. Clip Hedges. Gather the Black-cherrie and Morella Stones. Gather Mezerion berries. Gather the ſeeds of moſt Herbes and Flowers. Cut your Phyſick-herbes. In the beginning ſow Cabbage (thô I confeſs its too late. See the laſt moneth) Beets and Beet-card, Spinage, Black-radiſh, Chervil, Letice, Corn-ſallade, Endive, Scorzonera, Carvy, Marygold, Angelica, Scurvy-graſs, &c. Take up ripe Onions, Garleeks and Shallot, Unbind buds Inoculated. Cut and ſtring Strawberries. Lay July-flowers. Sow Columbines, Holyhoks, Larks-heells, Candytuffs, Popies, and ſuch as can endure Winter.

Take up your bulbs and plant as in the laſt. Sift the ground for Tulips and Gladiolus. Plunge in potted Annualls in Vacants. Keep down weeds by hawing, &c. Lay Graſs and Gravel, Beat, Roll, and mow well. Make Goosberrie and Curran Wines, &c.

Towards the end take Bees, take the lighteſt firſt; thoſe who are near heaths may differ a little. Deſtroy Waſps, ſtraiten the paſſage by putting on the hecks to ſecure from Robers.

Garden Diſhes and drinks in ſeaſon.

Many Pot-herbes and Sallades, Cabbage, Coleflower, Beet-card, Turneep, Radiſh, Carrot, Beet-rave, Scorzonera, Peas, Beans, and Kidnees, Artichocks, Cucumbers, Aples, Pears, Plumes, Apricocks, Geens, Goosberries, Currans, Raſps, Strawberries, &c.

Cyder, Metheglin, Cherrie Wine, Curran Wine, Goosberrie Wine, Raſpberrie Wine, &c.

SEP.

SEPTEMB.

FAllow, Trench, and level ground. Prepare pits and bordures for Trees. Gather plan feed, Almond, Peach, and white Plum Stones. Gather ripe Fruits. Plant furth Cabbage. Remove bulbs and plant them. Refresh, Trame, and House your tender Greens. Refresh and trim pots and cafes with July-flowers and other fine Flowers and plants, Carrying them to pits, shelter, and covert, giving them Air, &c.

Towards the end gather Safron.

Make Cyder, Perry, and other Wines, &c.

Straiten the entrance to Bee-hives, deftroy Wasps, &c.

Also you may now remove Bees.

Garden Dishes and drinks in feafon.

Varieties of Pot-herbes and Sallades, Cabbage, Cole-flower, Peas, Beans, and Kidnees, Artichocks, Beet-card, Beet-rave, Scorzonera, Carrots, Turneeps, Radifh, Cucumbers, Aples, Pears, Apricocks, Peaches, Nectarines, Quince, Grapes, Barberries, Filbeards.

Cyder, Liquorifh Ail, Metheglin, and Wine of Cherries, Rafps, Goolberries, Currans, &c.

OCTOBER.

GAther Winter Fruits. Trench and fallow grounds (mixing with proper soil) to ly over the Winter. Prepare dungs and mannures, mixing and laying them in heaps bottom'd and covered with Earth. Plant Hawthorn Hedges, And all Trees that lose their leaves; Also lay their branches. Prun Roses. Gather seeds of Hassell, Hawthorn, Plan, Ash, Beach, Oak, Aple, Pear, &c. Cut Strawberries, Artichocks, Asparagus, covering their beds with dung and Ashes. Earth up Winter Sallades, Herbes, and Flowers, a little. Plant Cabbage, &c. Plant Tulips, Anemonies, and other Bulbs. Sow the seed of Bairs-ears, Cowslips, Tulips, &c. Beat and Roll Gravel and Grass. Finish your last weeding and mowing. Lay bair lcopered Tree Roots and remove what harms them: also delve and dung such as require it. Drain excessive moisture wherever it be. Pickle and conserve Fruits. Make Perry and Cyder.

You may now safely remove Bees,

Garden Dishes and drinks in season.

Coleworts, Leeks, Cabbage, Cole-flowers, Onions, Shallot, Beans. Blanched Endive and Sellery. Pickled Asparagus, Purslain, &c.

Scorzonera, Beet-rave, Carrots, Turneeps, Parsneeps, Potatoes, Skirrets, Artichocks, Cucumbers, Aples, Pears, Plumes, Almond, &c.

Cyder, Perry, and Wine of Cherries, Currans, Goosberries, Rasberries, Ail of Liquorish, Metheglin, &c.

FINIS.